ECOLOGICAL DEVELOPMENT
IN POLAR REGIONS

A Study in Evolution

CONCEPTS OF MODERN BIOLOGY SERIES

Behavioral Aspects of Ecology, PETER H. KLOPFER
Ecological Development in Polar Regions: A Study in Evolution, M. J. DUNBAR
Euglenoid Flagellates, GORDON F. LEEDALE
Molecular Biology: Genes and the Chemical Control of Living Cells, J. M. BARRY
The Organism as an Adaptive Control System, JOHN M. REINER
Processes of Organic Evolution, G. LEDYARD STEBBINS

PRENTICE-HALL INTERNATIONAL, INC., *London*
PRENTICE-HALL OF AUSTRALIA, PTY. LTD., *Sydney*
PRENTICE-HALL OF CANADA, LTD., *Toronto*
PRENTICE-HALL OF INDIA PRIVATE LTD., *New Delhi*
PRENTICE-HALL OF JAPAN, INC., *Tokyo*

ECOLOGICAL DEVELOPMENT

IN POLAR REGIONS

A Study in Evolution

M. J. DUNBAR

McGill University

PRENTICE-HALL, INC., *Englewood Cliffs, N.J.*

Current printing (last digit):
10 9 8 7 6 5 4 3 2 1

Library of Congress Catalog Card Number: 68–16637

Printed in the United States of America

PREFACE

This short monograph took far longer to write than either the publisher or I anticipated, because what was at first a straightforward plan to bring together the basic results of several years of field work in Arctic and Subarctic waters developed into something a little more interpretative and general. It developed into a discussion of certain aspects of the present achievements of ecological research in polar regions, and of their general significance within the framework of contemporary ecological theory. The aspect with which I have always been principally concerned is the evolution of high latitude ecological systems, not the study of individual or specific adaptations.

The original title was to have been "Life Cycles at Low Temperatures," but as the content changes, so must the title. Other possibilities, such as "Polar Life" and "Sea, Ice, and Sex," were given short shrift; the spirit of the latter suggestion had already been preempted by two of my colleagues at McGill University, and in any case the accent on practical and theoretical ecology had to be strengthened.

One might think, and many do think, that the recent and present exciting developments in biology at the molecular and cellular levels would have pushed ecological research and speculation into the shadow. In some parts of the scientifically literate world this seems indeed to have happened, but certainly not in North America. On this continent it is fair to say that the most exciting developments in biology are at the two extremes of the size scale, the molecule and the ecosystem; and this is entirely appropriate, for it is a logical extension of that earlier period of evolutionary theory when the studies of Gregor Mendel appeared to be in collision course with the works of Darwin and Wallace.

The aura of molecular biology, however, and in particular the new magic of the DNA molecule, have perhaps blinded us from seeing that the real forum of organic evolution is not in DNA, nor in the cell, nor even in the individual organism, but in the forests, the savannahs, the

v

lakes, and the oceans; Professor G. E. Hutchinson has called it "the ecological theater and the evolutionary play." No matter what intricate changes take place in the chromosomes, the decision on whether or not a given variant population can become established in nature, perhaps to form a new species, is made at the level of the ecosystem.

This diversion of attention from nature in the wild, caused by laboratory science, has happened before, when the great achievements in physiology, comparative anatomy, embryology, and genetics in the late nineteenth and early twentieth centuries put the works of Darwin and Wallace for a time in the shadow. It was forgotten that the foundation of modern evolutionary theory rested upon natural history; the facts of biogeography, population dynamics, and the observation that "nature's one provision is to vary," as Eltringham put it. The stresses, the demands, and the elasticities of the environment, both living and nonliving, determine the process of speciation and of the growth of natural systems.

It is with this phase that I have been concerned here, specifically with reference to the polar regions, and with emphasis on the marine environments. This emphasis comes naturally from my own work which since 1936 has been in the cold salt water of Arctic and Subarctic Canada, Greenland, and Alaska. It is a pleasure to acknowledge the various sources of support and encouragement in that work, such as the Fisheries Research Board of Canada, the National Research Council, the Arctic Institute of North America, the Office of Naval Research, the Guggenheim Memorial Foundation, and the U. S. Steel Foundation, and, in the last analysis the most important of all, my own University; and to give special thanks to my friend and colleague, Dr. Ian McLaren, now of Dalhousie University and formerly of McGill, for much valuable criticism, discussion, and opposition, and for reading the manuscript.

M. J. DUNBAR

CONTENTS

| Chapter 1 | INTRODUCTION | 1 |

Chapter 2	HISTORICAL: TEMPERATURE EFFECTS	6
	Metabolism (Poikilotherms)	11
	Growth	18
	Cold Hardiness	22
	Homotherms	23

| Chapter 3 | THE PLEISTOCENE EVENT | 28 |

Chapter 4	ENVIRONMENT AND PRODUCTION IN POLAR REGIONS	36
	The Marine Environment	38
	The Environment of the Land	50
	Lakes	54

| Chapter 5 | ECOLOGICAL ADAPTATION AND EVOLUTION (I) | 56 |

Chapter 6	ECOLOGICAL ADAPTATION AND EVOLUTION (II)	68
	Adaptation to Environmental Oscillation	68
	Selection Toward Ecosystem Stability	72

Chapter 7	BIOGEOGRAPHY, SYSTEMATICS, AND ECOSYSTEM DEVELOPMENT	80
	Distributions	82
	Taxonomic Difficulties, "Phases," and "Morphs"	83
	Ecosystem Development	88

Chapter 8   REHEARSAL AND DISCUSSION   **92**

    Climate   93
    Habitat Variety   96
    Biomass and Productivity   98
    Predation and Competition   98
    Time   99

References   **101**

Indexes   **115**

Chapter 1
INTRODUCTION

Life in the polar regions has interested the civilized world for many centuries, first as an unfailing stimulant of wonder, as something essentially strange and exotic, later as a series of phenomena requiring serious attention, and finally as offering a special laboratory from which results of general significance can be elicited. As usually happens in scientific research, it has taken a long time for the real problems involved to present themselves, so that the really useful questions can be asked. It is with this last phase that we are concerned here.

Throughout this history of interest and of study, it has been assumed that the central problem was that presented by temperature, that the low temperature of polar environments controlled all facets of life in high latitudes, and that all the aspects in which Arctic and Antarctic life differed from life in lower latitudes could be ultimately explained in terms of temperature. Adaptation to low temperature was everything. There can be little doubt that temperature is important, especially in explanation at the proximate (as opposed to the ultimate) level, but it is one of the purposes of this book to suggest that this preoccupation with temperature has handicapped rather than helped, and that we have to examine the matter from new viewpoints, and with less unthinking acceptance of the nineteenth century assumption that what is true of nonliving things must also be true of living organisms. In particular, we must examine at least three other highly significant factors, namely the large amplitude of seasonal environmental oscillation in factors other than temperature, the generally low productivity (in the Arctic Ocean, for instance), and the youth of the ecosystem as a whole. None of these factors is directly related to temperature. After all, the difference between the temperatures of polar and tropical regions is not very large when they are compared on the absolute scale. This is especially true of aquatic environments, in which the difference is only of the order of 30°C, or between 303°K and 273°K approximately.

1

Possibly much of the confusion regarding temperature arises from the fact that at least some of the characteristics which do differentiate the environments of the high latitudes from those of the equatorial regions are related to the onset and persistence of the "glacial climate," a term which is quite obviously associated with temperature. The term, however, is even more obviously associated with ice, and sea ice has the effects both of reducing the penetration of light into the sea and of maintaining intense vertical stability, both of which are relevant to the production level. At all events, the climatic change which led to the Pleistocene placed adaptive demands upon living organisms, and the responses to those demands form our central study here.

Having said all this, it is nevertheless necessary to start the discussion with the temperature effect, and with living responses to changes in temperature. Low temperature is certainly one of the properties of the polar regions, and the problem of how living organisms have overcome, or sidestepped, the temperature laws which apply to nonliving systems must be both our starting point and perhaps the central thread of the argument. To the extent to which they have done so they have increased the significance of other limiting factors.

In this discussion, as in all consideration of biological events, it is essential that the distinction between proximate and ultimate effects be understood from the start, and the distinction maintained throughout. The terms *proximate* and *ultimate* are used here in an extension of their definition by Baker (1938) in relation to the study of breeding cycles and migration in birds; they correspond to the Aristotelian "efficient" and "final" causes. The proximate factors in the present context are those involved at the individual level, in such things as individual responses to temperature change or other environmental conditions. The distribution of many marine species, at any given time and in any given region, appears to be closely determined by temperature, that is to say that each species is viable only between certain specific limits of temperature, at least in a limited geographical region; and usually the limits for the developing eggs and young stages are narrower than those possible for the adults. Internal physiological or biochemical rhythms, as they exist in any individual, also belong to the proximate category. So do individual responses to light intensity or change in light intensity, length of day, or pressure conditions—in short any environmental factor to which the individual is attuned, or any individual reaction to the immediate condition.

Ultimate factors are those which have been responsible in the past for the evolution and maintenance of the proximate responses; they determine the function of the proximate effects in terms of the survival of the species, and form the framework of natural selection in which the proximate effects have developed. Since one must assume that change is constantly taking place, on the large time scale, in virtually all characteristics of virtually all species, it follows that the determining factors in the ultimate category must also be subject to change, and furthermore the phenomena of mutation and recombination of genetic material imply that there is an interplay between the two categories, so that the proximate can feed back to affect the ultimate. The ultimate factors are the determinants of the direction evolution takes at any given time, and they generally answer the question of what is the survival value, or the advantage to the species, of any response or condition at the proximate level.

Obviously these two levels of causation and of explanation are distinct. To fail to appreciate this is to introduce serious logical confusion. To use the example of specific geographic distribution once more, the ultimate determinants of distributional range are not the immediate environmental factors such as temperature, light, and humidity; they are to be found in ecological or competitive balance, the general and specific possibilities of the region concerned, and their most economical and advantageous exploitation. Many marine species come to the northern limits of their range in Baffin Bay, while others, fewer in number, extend farther north into pure Arctic water. The proximate causes of limitation may be the lowering of temperature northward, but the ultimate causes, which are usually more difficult to discover, have little to do with temperature as such. They involve rather the total ability of the environment to support a greater or lesser variety of species, or the necessity for high fecundity in an environment of such highly oscillating productivity as the Arctic, which in turn increases interspecific competition. This is discussed in Chapters 5, 6, and 8.

A third factor of great significance in determining the distribution and abundance of living things in different regions, and especially in polar regions, lies outside both the ultimate and the proximate categories. This is the factor of time, more particularly the time-lapse since some drastic environmental change such as the onset of glaciation, and it involves consideration of the age of the ecosystems themselves and their development from lesser to greater complexity. This matter is explored in a later chapter, but it should have introductory treatment here.

All creatures in the higher and middle latitudes live in an environment which is directly, either all the time or intermittently, influenced by the Pleistocene event; we are still living in an ice age in the sense of the Pleistocene period. There is an optimistic tendency in the lay mind to assume that the last ice recession heralded the final end of the glacial climates, but the evidence favours rather a return of the ice sheets in due course, the present being simply an interglacial phase in a series of oscillations. In any case certain polar regions, such as Greenland and Antarctica, are heavily glaciated at present and presumably have been for some million years, more or less. In terms of the age of the earth, however, and of the age of life on earth, this is an extremely short period. Adaptation to glacial climates is therefore not an ordinary necessity; both the problems and their solutions are recent, and it is reasonable to wonder whether the solutions are yet fully worked out. I have already drawn attention elsewhere (Dunbar 1963) to characteristics of the Arctic ecosystems which can perhaps best be interpreted as those of youth and immaturity, of imperfect adaptation to recent environmental change, and this whole subject will be reexamined and developed below.

Also by way of introduction, something must be said about the scope and purpose of the present study. It is not a review of our present knowledge of adaptations (or of acclimations or acclimatizations) * to low environmental temperatures. Many such reviews have appeared recently, all of them from the pens of physiologists, such as those of Bullock (1955), Fry (1958), and Burton and Edholm (1955). Nor is it a treatise in the style of the natural historian, descriptive of the Arctic fauna and of the many individual tricks to withstand cold conditions or to keep active in them. The approach is ecological, in the widest sense, and evolutionary, certainly ecological rather than physiological to the extent to which such a distinction makes sense, or can be used without affronting the physiologists who may feel that ecology *is* physiology. And so it is, in the strictly "autecological" phases and in part of the study of proximate causes (part only, for the proximate includes also the enormous field of the effects of one animal upon another, and of one species upon another, within the ecological system).

If the proximate aspects of ecology are partly physiological, the ultimate aspects are not. They belong to the study of evolution, and as such

---

* Fry (1958) points out, and goes far in resolving, the confusion of terms here. In particular, the term "adaptation" means one thing to the general biologist (associated with phylogenetic change), and something totally different to the physiologist (changes in the organism within a normal range and within the individual life, as the fisherman "adapts" to handling cold lines at sea, or as in Selye's "general adaptation syndrome"). With certain personal reservations, I intend to use as far as possible Fry's system of terminology: for short-term and fairly immediate changes in systemic and cellular mechanisms in response to given environmental changes or variations, *acclimation;* for longer-term responses which often last the life of the individual in a given population and which may be continued from one generation to another, *acclimatization;* for phylogenetic changes in which a given set or range of responses to the environment is fixed genetically, *adaptation.* Notice the avoidance of the objectionable term "adaption" and the fact that the differences between the three phenomena may be difficult to determine on even quite close inspection; in particular, the separation of acclimatization from adaptation will normally require considerable experimentation.

they touch closely upon the study of genetics and of systematics, and the "synecological" or ecosystem approach to the study of living nature. We are concerned here with both the proximate and the ultimate, but, since the emphasis is evolutionary, the latter must lend the more weight. We shall be examining the responses to the Pleistocene demands and challenges mainly in terms of ecosystem development, ecosystem limitation, and geographic distribution. Our purpose is to put Arctic life in its evolutionary perspective and to demonstrate that the Arctic has problems for life which extend considerably beyond ice, snow, and cold water.

Chapter 2

HISTORICAL: TEMPERATURE EFFECTS

Two histories affect our subject immediately, each in its own way—first the history of discoveries and interpretations concerning the effects of different temperatures and temperature change upon plants and animals, and second the history of the climatic change leading up to, and during, the Pleistocene period. The present chapter deals with the first, or scientific, history.

The importance of the environmental temperature was recognized in a general and intuitive way by the Greeks, rather in the psychological field than in the physiological. Empedocles, for example, made the interesting suggestion that men and women originated in areas of differing climates, women, the cold-blooded sex, in a northern climate, and men, of the warmer temperament, in the south. This of course raised the difficult problem of how each managed to appear and to survive independently, and at what fortunate point they finally met. In the same speculative and wholly fascinating category we must place the notion of "frozen words," which has a venerable history recently reviewed by Wilson and Rickard (1956). Plutarch attributed the following to a certain Antiphanes (quoted from Wilson and Rickard): "Antiphanes said humorously that in a certain city words congealed with the cold the moment they were spoken, and later, as they thawed out, people heard in the summer what they had said to one another in the winter; it was the same way, he asserted, with what was said by Plato to men still in their youth; not until long afterwards, if ever, did most of them come to perceive the meaning, when they had become old men." From that point on, frozen words appear at intervals in the literature of travellers' tales.

The Greeks were aware that life, especially poikilothermous life, was greatly slowed down and ultimately rendered dormant or extinguished by climatic extremes, but there is no record of any synthesis or formalization of these phenomena, and experimentation appears to have been largely foreign to the Greek temperament. They observed with great accuracy

6

and imagination, they produced brilliant speculative systems, and they excelled in mathematical presentation in patterns, or geometrically, but they did not discover the power of the experimental method.

This means in effect that there is nothing significant to record until well after the beginnings of modern science in the seventeenth century, specifically in the field of chemistry. The effects of heat, or more simply of flame, in cooking, in the working of metals, and in bringing comfort to humanity, like the grateful feel of sunshine upon the skin, had of course been known since prehistoric times, but the real nature of heat may well be said to have eluded our understanding even up to the present time, and it is clear that the difficulties involved in the physical and chemical understanding of heat have hardly, if at all, handicapped or slowed the progress of biology in studying the relevance of environmental heat to the life of organisms. It has been possible to measure temperature (heat intensity) accurately since the seventeenth century, which was all that really mattered, at least for the time being, to the biologist.

Physical and chemical understanding has been slow in coming. To quote William Cecil Dampier (1957): "The scientific concept of heat is derived from our sense-perception, and the thermometer enables us to define a scale with which to measure its intensity. Galileo invented the first thermometer and Amontons first used mercury. Different scales were introduced by Fahrenheit, Réaumur and Celsius. The idea of heat as a quantity was suggested by observations in distilleries, but it was Joseph Black (1728–99) who cleared up the still existing confusion between heat and temperature, calling them quantity and intensity of heat." In the seventeenth century both Boyle and Newton had suggested that heat should be considered as motion of the particles of substances, but this kinetic theory was discarded in favour of the notion that heat was a substance, or fluid (caloric theory), and was not reactivated until the development of the nineteenth century theory of energy, when both physics and chemistry began to take on a more modern look.

We are concerned here chiefly with two aspects: the reaction rate in relation to temperature, and the function of catalysts (since poikilothermous adjustment to low temperature must involve changes in enzymes, or the use of different enzymes), and in both subjects there is very little to report in the history of chemistry, as in biology, until quite recent time. According to Leicester (1956), the first chemical interpretation of catalysis was given by Désormes and Clément in 1806, describing the function of nitric acid in the manufacture of sulphuric acid. Berzelius, in 1836, reviewed a number of examples of catalysis without being able to offer any satisfactory theory to explain them. Finally, "the modern view of a catalyst as a substance that increases reaction rates without altering the general energy relations of a process was finally stated by the father of modern physical chemistry, Wilhelm Ostwald in 1894" (Leicester 1956). For our purposes we will have to accept that view without going more deeply into the chemistry of it.

The history of our knowledge of how temperature (heat intensity) affects reaction rates is extraordinarily difficult to extract from the general literature. Chemists seem to have been content to accept in a general and almost intuitive way the observation that rate and temperature are positively related, at least up to the first attempts to express the matter more precisely, by Van't Hoff (1884) and Arrhenius (1915). The "Van't Hoff rule," which should be accepted in general terms only, states that, within the temperature limits of the system, a rise of 10°C will increase the rate of reaction by a factor between 2 and 3. It was based originally on the chemical "law of mass action." It is not necessary here to go into the detail of the effects of temperature change on individual systems or individual organisms; many later approximations have been put forward, and the whole matter has been neatly and succinctly summarized by McLaren (1963). It lies outside the scope of this book.

It was long assumed that what was true of the chemistry of nonliving things must also be true for living organisms, and this strictly "mechanistic" assumption held firm up to the end of the nineteenth century and was not seriously challenged until long after that. Within certain limits this is still assumed by many, and within those limits the assumption is justified, but there is now general recognition that living organisms can take very important liberties with the strictly chemical laws.

It is necessary to separate at this point two historic lines, leading respectively to the study of the homotherms on the one hand and the poikilotherms on the other. This is obvious from the start; for the homotherms,* with active internal thermogenesis which maintains a steady pattern of body heat, the problems of dealing with cold climates are quite different from those facing the poikilotherms, and the scientific study of the two phenomena led into different paths and attracted different workers.

The study of thermogenesis in homotherms first enters a recognizably modern phase with Willis in 1670, as recorded by Smith and Hoijer (1962), whose paper is the most recent and the most complete review of the sub-

---

* I use the term *homotherm* throughout this book in preference to "homeotherm" or "homoiotherm." Although body heats in mammals and birds are not in fact completely steady with time, and although the temperature is different in different parts of the body, the recognition of these facts by strict etymological exactitude seems pedantic. Homotherm is good simple Greek and its meaning is accepted, together with the exceptions.

ject of cold acclimation in homotherms. Quoting from them: "Certainly the beginnings of a scientific rationale appeared as early as 1670 with Willis' theory that the 'vital heat' of the ancients arose in the blood from some sort of fermentation process involving the combination of chemical agents. Contemporaneously Mayow (1674) related animal thermogenesis analogously to a heat from chemical combustion, and he assigned to the lung the function, not of cooling the blood, but of facilitating the combustion process by atmospheric gas absorption."

For the poikilotherms, the first formal statement of the possible relation between heat and living activity appears to be the classic paper of Réaumur in 1735, in which he suggested that the time taken by plants in reaching a given stage, such as the ripening of the fruit, was related to the sum of the heat available during the growing season. This was the first statement of what are now known as *thermal constants* in the development of organisms, and implied that in fact the rate of development and the total heat, or sum of daily mean temperatures, were directly proportional. Precisely two hundred years later, in 1935, Bělehrádek, in his "Temperature and Living Matter," reviewed and developed the same principle at length, deriving useful generalizations from it. In the intervening two centuries, and also since 1935, great numbers of examples have been discovered and published of the apparently simple chemical relations of living creatures with respect to temperature, ranging from the pitch of the cricket's chirping, the heartbeats of *Daphnia,* and the speed of locomotion of *Amoeba,* to the cruising speed of goldfish and the metabolism of copepods. Reviews of this literature can be found in Allee *et al.* (1949), and elsewhere.

The direct relation between temperature and what can be lumped under "activity" (respiration, metabolism, locomotion, feeding rate, growth rate) was recognized as being so common and so widespread as to amount to a universal law, and like all such universal laws it was accepted by the uncritical as such. It suited the mechanistic leanings of much of biological science in the second half of the nineteenth century and the early part of the twentieth, and it was in tune with the spectacular advances made in the nonorganic sciences of physics and chemistry, which were well in the lead anyway. Furthermore, the relation is still unquestioned as far as individual and immediate responses are concerned; individual plants and poikilotherm animals do in fact behave in this way with respect to temperature, within their ecological ranges.

Doubts, however, began to appear at the end of the century. The Arctic fauna and flora were beginning to be examined critically, and it must have been clear to anyone working in that area that although growth is generally slower in cold climates than in temperate, some sort of adjustment of the temperature relation must occur, otherwise life in the Arctic, for poikilotherms, would be an impossibility. The observations and measurements which led to the generality of the activity-temperature relation were done in temperate regions of civilization and upon animals and plants adjusted to the local conditions. If the temperature-activity curves were extrapolated downward to the cold conditions of the polar climates, the organisms concerned would obviously not have functioned at all. Arctic species must have different and lower ecological temperature ranges and therefore some biochemical adjustment must have been made. This was especially remarkable when two closely related forms were compared, or two populations of the same species, temperate and polar, as for instance populations of the speckled trout at opposite ends of its north-south range. The same was true for tropical species, in which adjustment upward occurred. The Q-10 law could no longer be taken at face value, without question and without modification. Allowances in fact had to be made for the heretical capabilities of living, as opposed to nonliving, systems.

It followed that the generally held opinion—an opinion still found among many mammalian physiologists—that the poikilotherms are at the mercy of the environmental temperature required reexamination. The first suggestion of this necessity is probably to be found in a paper by Krehl and Soetbeer (1899) [see Bullock (1955), p. 313] who suggested that (to quote from Bullock) "in respect of temperature poikilotherms were not simple 'Spielbälle der Umgebung' but showed metabolic adaptation of their protoplasm." Bullock quotes Krogh (1916) as being aware that such regulation might be expected; Krogh wrote: "It would be interesting to compare the respiratory exchange in such cases" (poikilotherms living in colder and warmer waters) "because it would appear unlikely from a teleological point of view that it should differ so much as would be ordinarily implied from the temperature difference. One would expect that animals living at a very low temperature should show a relatively high standard metabolism at that temperature compared with others living normally at a high temperature" (Krogh 1916).

This brings our history to the point of departure of the "temperature compensation" studies summarized by Bullock (1955), Dunbar (1957), and Fry (1958), all in the field of zoology rather than botany. In this section I am drawing largely upon my own 1957 paper. There does not appear to be much evidence of temperature compensation in plants, even in the phytoplankton; this might well be a useful subject for investigation. Considering, however, that plants obtain their energy directly from the sun this is perhaps not surprising, for at the proximate level temperature compensation is basically a matter of the uses to which the available energy is put. Animals, which obtain all their energy from food, in fact from plants in the short or the long run, base their internal economy upon the food supply, and if the food supply is low, as it appears to be in the higher and middle latitudes during a considerable part of the year, the energy must be shared between a number of processes (Fig. 1) whose rates will be dictated by the immediate or seasonal requirements of the species, and the pattern of the sharing will therefore be established at the ultimate level, according to the criteria of survival and the possibilities of the total environment. The relative demands of the processes concerned are not the same in all environments, or in all animal groups, or at all times of year. It has long been recognized that the locomotor ac-

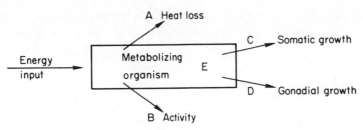

FIG. 1   Energy pathways in an organism (see text).

tivity and speed of poikilotherms living in very cold regions are much greater than the Q-10 rule applied to animals living in temperate regions would lead us to expect. There must therefore be regulation of the determinants of activity which allow the unexpectedly high level in cold climates. Such regulation may be, for all that is at present known about it, either genetically established (adaptation) or a matter of individual ontogenetic adjustment (acclimation or acclimatization); but it is not difficult to imagine the high probability of the true (genetic) evolution of such regulation, in view of its obvious high selective value. A minimum, and a high minimum, of general muscular activity is required for the business of food-getting and of escaping from predators, especially those which are not bound by this temperature condition, namely homotherms.

Metabolism (Poikilotherms)

Regulation in locomotor activity with respect to temperature does not necessarily mean that there must be a corresponding regulation in resting metabolism, but regulation in resting metabolism is common, and is well established in the literature. Among the pioneers in the field are Fox (1936, 1939) and Wingfield (1939); also Fox and Wingfield (1937) in England, and Thorson (1936, 1950, 1952) and Spärck (1936) in Denmark. Thorson, studying the metabolic rates (measured by oxygen consumption) of inshore molluscs in northeast Greenland, Denmark, and the Persian Gulf, found that the rates were very nearly equal in the same species or in closely related species living in the three regions, each being measured at its normal environmental temperature; if the Arctic individuals

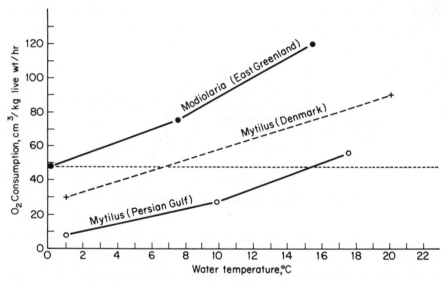

FIG. 2 Oxygen consumption of adult mytilids fom high Arctic, boreal, and tropical waters. Redrawn from Thorson (1952). Each population in its own natural environment has approximately the same metabolic rate as the others, indicated by the horizontal dashed line.

were placed in water of temperature corresponding to the Danish environment, their metabolic rates rose to levels considerably higher than those of the Danish form, and the same, *mutatis mutandis,* for the Persian and Danish populations (Fig. 2).

Somewhat different results were obtained by Fox and Wingfield. Fox (1936), working on the oxygen consumption of pairs of species (each pair being in the same genus) of echinoderms, annelids, and crustaceans, found that "for seven pairs of species inhabiting respectively English waters and more northern seas (Kristineberg in Sweden), the oxygen consumption of the warmer-water species is greater than that of the colder-water species (measured at the normal temperatures at which each species lives) although the locomotory activity of the former is apparently no greater." Fox suggested "that the similar locomotory activities of the two species require approximately equal amounts of oxygen, but that the non-locomotory oxygen consumption of the warmer-water species is higher than that of the cold-water species." Fox thus suggested in effect that the available energy must be shared between different vital processes, as described above, and appears to have assumed either that the available energy was less in the cooler water or that the animals lived at a lesser rate than those in the warmer region.

The same results were obtained for two species of prawns (Fox and Wingfield 1937). In this 1937 paper there is a note on the work of Spärck and Thorson, which appeared at the same time. Fox and Wingfield, commenting on the disagreement between their results and those of the two Danish workers, pointed out that Spärck and Thorson had used lamellibranchs, which were not used in the English work. However, Thorson (1952) and also Berg (1953) showed that the animals used in Fox's work were not truly comparable owing to differences in size and age, and that if these factors were taken into account, then metabolic regulation in the Kristineberg material was in fact demonstrated.

Wingfield (1939) emphasized the danger of drawing too firm conclusions from comparisons of two different species, no matter how closely related, by demonstrating that if the polychaete *Pectinaria granulata* from east Greenland is compared with *P. auricoma* from Millport it does not show metabolic regulation, but if compared with *P. koveni,* also from Millport, it does show regulation. Scholander, Flagg, Walters, and Irving (1953), using this same technique of comparing more or less closely related groups from Tropics and Arctic, found that in certain Crustacea there is evidence of metabolic regulation or compensation, the Arctic forms showing somewhat higher metabolism than would have been expected by simple extrapolation from the tropical performances.

Demeusy (1957) found that in the fiddler crab *Uca pugilator,* which has a wide distribution in latitude, populations from Woods Hole responded somewhat differently to temperature than did the populations from Florida (the measurements were made at 1.4°C and 15°C). The northerly population showed considerably higher metabolism at the lower temperature, was less sensitive to temperature change (that is, had a lower Q_{10}), and was more resistant to low temperatures, than the Florida group. Demeusy comments that such differences might be used to distinguish two subspecies of *Uca pugilator.*

This work has been done mainly on shallow-water benthonic species, which are the easiest to handle in the laboratory and are easily obtained. Very little work has been done on planktonic forms, principally because they are difficult to maintain and cultivate in laboratory conditions. Pioneer studies by Conover (1959, 1960, 1962) on copepods are available, but there is nothing from Arctic or tropical water with which to compare his results. An important paper has recently appeared by McWhinnie (1964) on metabolic temperature responses in the euphausid *Euphausia superba* in the Antarctic; here again, but in reverse, we have nothing from temperate or Arctic euphausids for comparison. McWhinnie has established that *Euphausia superba* is a highly specialized species, adapted to maximum efficiency in water very close to the freezing point. In this it resembles Antarctic fishes so far examined (see below). Under laboratory conditions, *E. superba* showed greatest activity and lowest mortality at $-1.5°C$, showed very low Q_{10} values in the range $0–5°C$ (Q_{10} 1.1 to 1.3), and more normal values (2.1) between $5°C$ and $15°C$, when measured immediately after collection. It thus showed metabolic independence (of temperature) within the temperature range of its normal environment south of the Antarctic Convergence. No such results have been obtained for Arctic organisms, in which the individual Q_{10} values measured have been usually between 2 and 3, and sometimes as high as 4.5 (see, for instance, Scholander *et al.* 1953).

In the poikilothermous vertebrates, Fry (1951 and elsewhere) has shown that the speckled trout (*Salvelinus fontinalis*) is capable of limited metabolic acclimation under laboratory conditions, but there is no evidence yet that an established acclimatization or adaptation exists in populations living in very cold water. Power (unpublished data) has found only very low standard metabolic rates, showing little or no regulation, in speckled trout at the northern limit of distribution in northern Quebec. On the other hand Scholander *et al.* (1953), comparing tropical with Arctic fishes (interspecific and intergeneric comparison), found considerable compensation, the Arctic species and genera lying in an intermediate position with respect to oxygen consumption between the tropical fish and the expected or extrapolated position (the Krogh line) for fish at $0°C$. Peiss and Field (1950) compared the oxygen consumption of excised brain and liver tissue of the polar cod (*Boreogadus saida*) with that of the golden orfe (*Idus melanotus*), and found that the Q_{10} values for the cod tissues remained steady over the experimental temperature range of $0–25°C$, whereas the values for the orfe tissue increased markedly below $10°C$. This resulted in oxygen consumption values for the polar cod several times as great as in the orfe at low temperatures, but the experiments in fact showed a breakdown in the metabolic balance in the orfe, the warmer-water form, at low temperatures, rather than any metabolic regulation in the cod.

Wohlschlag, in a series of papers on Arctic and Antarctic fishes (for bibliography and general discussion see Wohlschlag 1964), has made some significant advances, which may be summarized as follows:

1. The Alaskan Arctic whitefish *Coregonus sardinella* has both migrant and nonmigrant populations, the former showing somewhat higher metabolic rates than the resident form, which in turn is considerably fatter. This is relevant to the whole question of migration in high-latitude animals which is touched upon in Chapter 8.

2. Standard metabolism in a sluggish benthonic Antarctic fish, the nototheniid *Trematomus bernacchii,* is comparatively high at normal environmental temperatures (below 0°C), higher than those measured for Arctic fishes, and much higher than the extrapolated values for temperate species. Above 0°C, the metabolism falls, showing extreme cold stenothermy.

3. One Antarctic benthonic fish, a zoarcid, *Rigophila dearborni,* was shown to have an extremely low metabolism, lying very close to the Krogh line of standard metabolism. The zoarcids are typically north temperate and Subarctic in distribution; possibly this new species is a recent arrival in the very cold Antarctic waters. The contrast between the adapted forms and the nonadapted species is shown in Fig. 3, taken from Wohlschlag (1963).

4. At the normal environmental temperature, which is very low (down to −1.9°C), the level of energy required for swimming is "at least double" the values for more temperate species; Wohlschlag suggested that this is in response to high viscosity.

5. From his own work and that of others, Wohlschlag concluded that "there is a marked metabolic range attenuation due to cold adaptation and upward displacement of metabolic levels for polar species that are stenothermally adapted to temperatures at or below zero degrees" (Wohlschlag (1964). This narrowing of the ecological temperature range is discussed again below as a factor in the apparent absence, or rarity, of migration in polar fishes.

6. There is a high metabolic variability at low temperatures, both in cold-adapted species and in temperate species measured at low temperatures, which has so far not been correlated with any possible cause, but which may be related to different temperature coefficients in different tissues of the body.

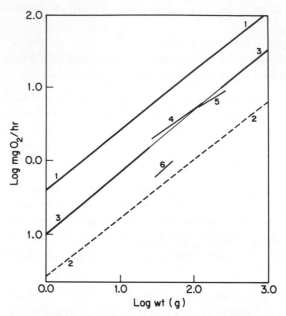

FIG. 3 Metabolic levels in fishes, from Wohlschlag (1963). Following description fom Wohlschlag: "Line 1—average metabolism at 20° for 369 temperate marine and fresh-water fishes (approximately 100 species) from Winberg (1956). Line 2—same as Line 1 but reduced to 0° by extrapolation along Krogh's (1916) curve of standard metabolism. Line 3—average metabolism for 4 species of arctic fish at 0° from Scholander *et al.* (1953). Lines 4 and 5—respective male and female metabolic levels of antarctic *Trematomus bernacchii* at —1.8° from Wohlschlag (1962). Line 6—metabolic level of new antarctic zoarcid species at —1.8° from the present study."

The general known relations between metabolism and temperature for tropical, temperate, and polar fishes, redrawn from Wohlschlag (1964), are shown in Fig. 4.

From the work so far done it is apparent that with a few exceptions Arctic and Antarctic poikilotherms, more especially the planktonic and nektonic forms, show normal high activity, similar to the activity levels of temperate and tropical forms, and that it is usual to find regulation, whether acclimatization or adaptation, in standard metabolism. How these effects are achieved is not understood, although it is probably safe to say that the processes involve changes in the enzymes employed. It is not even clear whether we may legitimately assume, because polar waters are colder than tropical, that it follows that the polar systems operate at lower energy levels. If we could assume this, then it would follow from the argument presented graphically in Fig. 1 that the energy used in

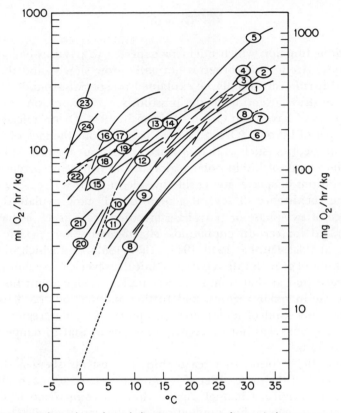

FIG. 4 Relationships of metabolism to temperature for tropical, temperate, and polar fishes weighing about 5 grams, redrawn from Wohlschlag (1964), with permission. Lines 1–5, tropical species; lines 6–14, temperate; lines 15–19, Antarctic. For details of species, see Wohlschlag 1964, p. 57.

maintaining high metabolic rates and high locomotor activity in polar regions must be used at the expense of some other part of the system. An animal is an open system, part of a larger pattern, and it obtains its own energy from the environment. It is true, however, that in Arctic and Antarctic water, and in Subarctic and temperate water also, the food production is low during the winter, and for most of the year in the case of the pure Arctic water. Whether from a direct temperature effect, or from low food supply over the year, we may take it that the conservation of energy is an important problem for polar animals. It must therefore follow that if high activity is to be maintained it will be at the expense of other processes.

Growth

One obvious function which might be expected to pay this energy bill is growth rate. Arctic poikilotherms normally grow slowly, and the exceptions to this rule can usually be explained on special grounds. The first biologist to draw attention to the possibility of "adaptation" in growth rates appears to have been Orton. Writing in 1923, Orton referred to an earlier paper of his own (Orton 1920) as pointing out the lack of evidence bearing on theories [such as that of Loeb (1908)] put forward "to explain (a) the abundance of life in polar regions,* and (b) the occurrence of several generations of species living side by side in polar waters." This latter point, the coexistence of several generations, is now explained by the prevalence of two-phase or polyphase breeding cycles, such as have been demonstrated for certain euphausids, chaetognaths, and pelagic amphipods (Ruud 1932, Dunbar 1940, 1946a, 1957, 1962), and which in fact are the result not of growth rate regulation, but the reverse (very slow growth). Orton urged that at that time there was no knowledge about the growth of organisms in polar regions, and further pointed out (as Krogh had done) that "the kind of metabolism of animals in polar regions and in deep-sea situations was not necessarily the same as that in temperate and tropical regions."

Orton (1923) found that sea urchins in west Spitsbergen showed a rate of growth of the same order as is found in related forms in Plymouth waters in the English Channel. Again, this is a comparison of different species, not of geographic populations of the same species.† Thorson (1936) found slow "unregulated" growth rates in lamellibranchs in east Greenland, and concluded provisionally "that the bottom invertebrates

---

* "The abundance of life in polar regions" was a phrase used in former decades to give expression to the high production apparent in commercial species in Subarctic (not Arctic) water and in the Antarctic. Definitions of "Arctic" and "Subarctic" regions, which regions are greatly different from each other in the sea, and discussion of the factors of productivity, will be found in Chap. 4.

† After several centuries of effort, it is doubtful whether the term "species" is any more precise now than it was in the fifteenth century. Systematics have come full circle. Whether individuals, apparently morphologically identical, but living in different climates and showing considerable differences in growth rate, breeding cycle, metabolic rates, fecundity, and egg size and number can properly be considered to belong to the same species depends on the biologist examining the problem. The relevance of systematics to the general subject of this book is discussed in Chapter 7. It is a matter both of great importance and no importance, depending on your point of view; the real trouble began with the excellent Linnaeus, who gave us a taxonomic method expressly designed for a static system, which we now insist on trying to adapt to what we know perfectly well is not static at all.

in the northeast Greenland seas will on the whole have a slow growth, a long life, and a late maturity which means that the production must be extremely small." In a later paper (1950), however, he recorded remarkably rapid growth in *larval* stages, and having already found metabolic regulation in the Arctic molluscs, decided that adaptive regulation of both growth and metabolism were normal in the Arctic, and generally accepted, and discarded his former conclusions and those of Wimpenny (1941) as being out of date. Wimpenny, in a paper on "organic polarity," had assumed that life cycles were shorter in tropical than in polar waters, which indeed they are.*

Special considerations have been applied to the growth rates of pelagic larval stages of Arctic benthonic invertebrates. Thorson has shown that in many species the larval life in the coldest waters is as short as is larval life in tropical waters, about three weeks in some species, and explains this at the ultimate level as the result of necessity. The period of high phytoplankton production in the high-Arctic water is very short, especially in fjord waters, owing to the rapid achievement of physical stability caused by meltwater and the consequent intense density stratification. It is therefore essential that planktonic larval stages be completed by the end of this period of food production, and in fact most cold-water benthonic forms have, as it were, taken the easier solution of eliminating the larval stage altogether, the implication being that this is more economical or less difficult than adjusting the larval growth rate (Thorson 1950). A high growth rate in larval development was also found by Fox (1938) in sea urchins, those from British waters growing faster than those of the Mediterranean, at given temperatures, and fast larval growth was recorded by Dehnel (1955) in gastropod molluscs in southeastern Alaska, in which the growth was in fact from two to nine times more rapid than for populations of the same species in southern California. In these experiments species with yolky telolecithal egg masses were chosen in order to minimize the importance of food availability; Dehnel made the suggestion that factors other than temperature might have been responsible for the fast growth of the Alaskan larvae. It should also be pointed out, in passing, that the surface temperatures in southeast Alaska are not low compared with Arctic or even Subarctic regions; for example, the annual range at Sitka is approximately from 4°C to 15°C.

---

* There is an ambiguity in the use of the term *growth*. During the growing season, when food is abundant, there is evidence that growth in polar regions can be as fast as anywhere else. But the term is also applied to the time required to reach maturity in a given environment, which is a function of the relation between the length of the growing period and the length of the resting period or period of very slow growth, within the annual cycle. Obviously, it is in this latter sense that the term is used here.

Fast larval (embryonic) growth in the colder part of the range has also been reported in the Amphibia, by Moore (1939), who showed that the development of species of the genus *Rana* is faster, the colder the environment. The northern *Rana sylvatica* was found to develop at about twice the rate of the southern *Rana catesbiana*. At the extreme north of its range, on the shores of Ungava Bay, *Rana sylvatica* is able to develop to metamorphosis in the short season available (Hildebrand 1949).

Surprisingly fast growth, at least up to sexual maturity, has been recorded in three nototheniid fishes in the Antarctic (Olsen 1955). All three are active species, and at their environmental temperatures close to 0°C they grow faster than northern Alaskan *Coregonus sardinella* at temperatures well above zero (Wohlschlag 1960). Here we have a case of fast growth and high activity together, which caused Wohlschlag to put the question to which there is at present no answer: "Is there a possibility of an increased efficiency of energy conversion into growth from warmer to polar waters in the same sense that there is cold adaptation?"

However, such regulation in growth rate in low temperatures is the exception rather than the rule, and applies usually to the larvae so far as we know. All authors have assumed, and some have shown, that in general growth is very slow in the Arctic and Antarctic. Dehnel (1955) wrote: "Generally, the assumption is made that species of marine poikilotherms which inhabit the colder waters of the higher latitudes grow more slowly, grow to a larger size, and have a greater longevity than individuals of the same or closely related species from warmer waters." This is in fact more than an assumption; there is a great deal of evidence in the literature for the slowing down of growth rates in cold water as compared with warm, not only in the comparison of different species within one genus but also of different populations of the same species, and some of it is of long standing. Schneider (1891), for example, found that several of the common gammarid amphipods of the Tromsö coast have a two-year life cycle, some even longer, and commented that increase in lifetime, and time required to reach maturity, with increasing geographic latitude was well-known in other poikilotherms, including insects. Among the Lepidoptera many species have a one-year life cycle in Germany and a two-year cycle in Norway. Schneider mentioned also the tiger moth, *Arctia caja,* which lives one year in the Oslo area but requires two years at Tromsö. These and many other examples raise the interesting point, discussed below, that the "choice" between a one- or a two-year cycle is "all or nothing"; no intermediate length of life is possible, or at least probable, within the annual seasonal framework. This is a good example of the ultimate level of causation (necessity to adjust to the length of the year) controlling the selection of responses at the proximate level (adjustment of growth rate to temperature or other external immediate factor). I know of no example, though examples may well exist, of both one- and two-year cycles being found in the same species in the same area.

Other cases of longer life in lower temperature should be included in this historical review: In the chaetognath *Sagitta elegans,* Russell (1932) recorded four and perhaps five succeeding broods produced in one year at Plymouth, each brood being parental to the next. In the same species in the Canadian eastern Arctic, Dunbar (1941, 1962) found the life cycle to be two years. Bogorov (1940) recorded a two-year cycle for both *Sagitta elegans* and *Eukrohnia hamata* in the Barents Sea. In the Euphausiacea, Macdonald (1928) described a probable one-year life in *Thysanoessa raschii* in the Clyde sea area, and Einarsson (1945) also found a one-year cycle in the same species in southern Icelandic waters, but concluded that in northern Iceland and in west Greenland *T. raschii* took two years to reach maturity; the same conclusion was reached by Dunbar (1940) for both *T. raschii* and *T. inermis* in west Greenland (Disko Bay). The same length of life was found for *T. raschii* and *T. longicaudata* in the Barents Sea by Bogorov (1940). In the deep-water shrimp *Pandalus borealis,* Hjort and Ruud (1938) found that maturation (to maleness) occurred in the second summer of life in Norway, whereas Rasmussen (1942) described a three-year maturity age in Spitsbergen.

The copepod *Calanus finmarchicus (sensu lato)* has been exhaustively examined, and the research recently reviewed by Marshall and Orr (1955), who wrote (p. 64): "As is natural, the lower the temperature the slower is the rate of development, and the later does the first spawning occur." In the Clyde sea area, where the temperature at the time the water is homothermic is about 7°C, *C. finmarchicus* spawns at least three times during the period between mid-February and late July. The life span is thus about two months in spring. The winter stock may live up to seven months. In Scoresby Sound, east Greenland, where the winter temperature is about -1.5°C for more than half the year, the same species spawns only once a year; there is evidence that some of the population may survive a second winter. In Ungava Bay, Fontaine (1955) recorded one-year life cycles in both *Calanus finmarchicus* and *Pseudocalanus minutus.* Other planktonic copepods follow the same pattern. Digby (1954) commented that in view of this great extension of life cycle, copepods cannot be considered to be particularly well adapted to living in cold water, a comment which we shall have to discuss at greater length later. In the extremely oligotrophic waters of Tanquary Fjord in Ellesmere Island Cairns (1965) finds that *Pseudocalanus* extends its life beyond the one year found in Ungava Bay, taking two years to reach maturity, and that the genus *Calanus* takes longer still.

An exception to this rule of slower growth in colder water was published by Moore (1934), who found that the barnacle *Balanus balanoides* grows faster at Herda, Norway, than at Port Erin in the Irish Sea, where in turn it grows faster than at St. Malo in France.

The same general pattern has been found for the fishes. The female Arctic Char (*Salvelinus alpinus*) in Frobisher Bay, Baffin Island, takes twelve years to reach maturity (Grainger 1953), compared with much shorter periods farther south. Whitefish in Great Slave have a two-year period to maturity as compared with three years in Great Bear Lake. The Atlantic cod *(Gadus morhua)* that spend the summer in northeast Ungava Bay (Port Burwell) grow much more slowly than the cod of west Greenland, Newfoundland, or Nova Scotia.

To sum up this part of the history, the early belief that poikilothermous animals must obey the physico-chemical laws relating to temperature strictly, and precisely as do nonliving systems, gave way at the beginning of this century, although very gradually and unwillingly, partly in the light of the first critical work on polar faunas. It has become clear from studies made in the last thirty years that regulation of one sort or another, whether temporary or permanent (by genetic change), in standard metabolism, is the rule, and that this applies both to pairs or complexes of species within one genus and to different geographic populations within the same species. Regulation of any significance in growth rate, however, appears to be found only where special necessities at the ultimate level exist, as in the growth of pelagic larvae of benthonic invertebrates. It is not yet clear whether slow growth is a necessity forced upon the polar organisms by energy requirements for other purposes, or whether the slow growth itself is a form of adaptation to the ecological situation. This is discussed further in Chapters 5 and 6.

Cold Hardiness

Under this somewhat imprecise heading come special capabilities of animals and plants to survive temporary cold conditions, Arctic, alpine, or other. They are generally accepted as true adaptations involving in each case an evolved genetic modification. The wintering of insects, desiccation in certain primitive invertebrate phyla, withstanding of freezing in intertidal animals, hibernation in certain homotherms, and the existence of some antifreezing ability in Arctic fishes, are all included here. They are all extremely interesting physiologically but not in the main stream of the present thesis. In all except the last case, a state of dormancy is induced, and the term "cold hardiness" is not normally used to include the ability of certain Arctic and Antarctic birds and mammals to live happily and actively in those environments the whole year round.

Many species in several groups are capable of special adaptations which make it possible for them to avoid cold death by special means. To quote from Allee *et al.* (1949): "It is probably not an overstatement to summarize our knowledge of cold death by saying . . . that, with the exception of a few organisms that are killed at temperatures above zero (Celsius), plants and animals of the temperate latitudes either die when chilled relatively near to their freezing points or are not killed by any low temperature to which they may be subjected in nature." Each of these tricks of physiological adaptation could form, and some have formed, the subject of whole books; in the present context it is enough simply to note that they are general phenomena in those terrestrial poikilotherms which withstand temperate and polar winters. True hibernation in homotherms is a phenomenon of temperate rather than higher latitudes, since frost-free refuges are not to be found in Arctic and Antarctic regions. The inferred existence of "antifreezing" ability in Arctic fishes is a new discovery (Scholander *et al.* 1957). Deep-water Arctic fishes can apparently remain supercooled, below the blood freezing point, indefinitely; surface living forms, such as the Greenland cod (*Gadus ogac*) and the shallow-water sculpin *Myoxocephalus scorpius,* for which supercooling is impossible owing to the hazard of ice nuclei in the water, have been shown to raise the osmotic pressure of the blood by the secretion into it of a substance as yet unidentified. Scholander and his co-workers were able to show experimentally that ice nuclei in the water penetrated the integument of the fish; or, to be more precise, that the presence of ice nuclei in a supercooled external medium caused the freezing of the fluids of the fish exposed to them.

Homotherms

Apart from the special case of hibernation, which is not a polar phenomenon at all, the study of general metabolic, biochemical, and morphological changes in relation to low environmental temperature in homotherms has shown, as might be expected, that if the problems for poikilotherms are apparently fairly easily solved, those of the homotherms are simpler still. The evolution of homothermy in the Mesozoic made adjustment to climatic changes relatively easy to achieve; in the case of the Pliocene-Pleistocene change, the problem was twofold: (1) to avoid excessive loss of heat, and still make heat loss possible when it is necessary, and (2) to maintain the proper functioning of nerves and muscles in peripheral and distal regions of the body. These problems are solved by insulation, the adjustment of body size and body proportions, heat exchanger systems in the blood circulation, adaptation in the conductivity of nerves, and changes in the melting points of fats.

Hibernation, by which is meant the state of dormancy entered into by certain mammals and a very few species of birds in temperate regions in which the environment offers frost-free refuges, may be looked upon as the lazy way of avoiding either migration or the maintenance of winter activity. Birds can fly, and therefore the phenomenon of hibernation is very rare in birds, as is also the habit of remaining in the polar regions in the winter. The simplest way to deal with the winter cold and absence of readily available food is to move toward the equator, and this is what most Arctic birds do. Penguins in the Antarctic have developed highly efficient insulation and they are marine feeders, so that their food supply is assured provided they stay close to the shore or the ice edge. The mammals of the Arctic, which are few in number to begin with, remain active during the winter, exploiting the food supply beneath the snow and along the seashore. Indeed, they must do so, for there are no frost-free refuges to permit hibernation and they are not equipped to migrate with the necessary speed.

As regards special adaptations, acclimations, and acclimatizations in homotherms to meet cold conditions, it is probably best to begin, historically, with two "rules" which gained perhaps rather more importance in the ecological texts than they may deserve: the Bergmann rule and Allen's rule.

The Bergmann rule, as interpreted today, is based upon the principle that while heat production in a homotherm is three-dimensional, and proportional to the mass of the metabolizing substance, the loss of heat occurs at the surface, and is thus a two-dimensional affair. In a cold environment, therefore, where heat conservation becomes vitally important, larger animals have an advantage over smaller ones owing to their smaller surface/mass ratio. Hence there should be a tendency for a given species (or other taxonomic group) to evolve larger body size in the colder parts of its range. Bergmann (1847) offered this as an empirical rule derived from observation, and in fact many groups of mammals and birds obey it. Hesse, Allee, and Schmidt (1951) give the penguins as a good example, and quote several others. It was put forward originally as applying intraspecifically only.

There are many exceptions to the rule, such as the varieties of caribou, certain grouse, racoons, and otters, and there is some evidence that the Bergmann effect is environmentally controlled in some cases—that is, it is not an adaptation in the sense used here, but rather an acclimatization. One good example of the waywardness of the rule has been given by Salomonsen (1950), concerning the ringed plover. The ringed plover has been reported as an exception to the Bergmann rule in that the smaller varieties, or stocks, breed farthest north. Salomonsen pointed out that the populations which breed farthest north migrate to the most southerly (warmest) parts of the specific winter range, so that the species obeys the rule in winter but disobeys it in summer.

The Bergmann rule should not, in fact, be taken too seriously. Attention has been drawn by Scholander (1955) to its shortcomings: "The hopeless inadequacy of cold adaptation via Bergmann's rule may be seen by the following consideration. Take a body-to-air gradient in the tropics of 7° and in the Arctic of 70°, i.e. a tenfold increase. A tenfold greater cooling in the Arctic animal is prevented by covering the surface with fur a few centimeters thick. A relative surface reduction of ten times would require a weight increase of the animal of one thousand times."

Body size as such is only one character toward which selection may or may not operate, and it may prove to be an advantage or disadvantage with respect to factors other than temperature. As a means of dealing with low environmental temperature, large bulk must be considered relatively unimportant. "From a purely physiological standpoint, if relative surface reduction were a point of general adaptive importance, we should expect this to modify the animals not only on a sub-specific level, but the whole northern warm-blooded fauna should by convergence tend towards large globular species. This quite obviously is not so" (Scholander 1955).

Mayr (1956), in replying to Scholander's criticisms of the Bergmann rule, pointed out that the rule is empirical only, and that the physiological interpretation of the rule is a separate matter. Newman (1956) discusses both Bergmann's and Allen's rule (see below) with special reference to man, and concludes that both rules hold well: "If anything, these rules seem to be more closely operative in man than in other species of homeotherms." Rensch (1959) summarizes a number of studies on the subject, including many of his own, and does not hesitate either to uphold the Bergmann rule or to give it the normal interpretation in terms of selective advantage with respect to cold climates. There is no disagreement, however, on the other facet of the problem, namely that there are other and more effective anatomical adaptations to cold than reduction in the surface-to-bulk ratio.

Allen's rule (Allen 1877) is almost as venerable as the Bergmann principle, and has the same empirical basis and the same limitations. It states that in cold environments there is a tendency for the development of shorter and more compact extremities, such as ears, limbs, tails, and snouts, and is illustrated in a number of groups including the rabbits and hares, wolves and foxes, and the rodents. There are also exceptions to the rule: the longest neck, head, and snout among the Ursidae, for instance, are found in the polar bear. The rule implies a reversal of the normal allometric consequences to be expected to follow from the Bergmann rule.

Both these rules concern body size or shape in relation to the external, or environmental, temperature. A relation between size and *internal* temperature has been pointed out by Rodbard (1950), in a paper which has considerable relevance to the matter in hand. The body temperatures of birds are higher than those of mammals, but this appears to be be-

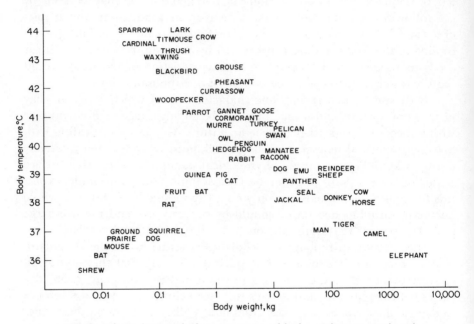

FIG. 5   Relation between body temperature and body weight in mammals and birds; from Rodbard (1950).

cause mammals, in the size range in which most birds exist, fail to maintain the temperature trend established by the mammals themselves in the size range above that of birds. The relation is shown in Fig. 5, modified from Rodbard.

For the larger mammals, down to approximately 10 kilograms in weight, there is a straight-line inverse relationship between body temperature and the logarithm of the adult weight, but between 10 kilograms and 1 kilogram this relationship is lost and replaced, for the smaller mammals down to the limit of small size, by a positive, or direct, straight-line correspondence. The straight-line inverse relationship shown by the larger mammals, however, is taken over and continued by the birds. To be true to the fashion of named rules, this should perhaps be christened "Rodbard's rule."

The explanation of this is probably to be found in the lesser insulating capacity of fur as compared with feathers, and the high metabolism required to maintain body heat in small homotherms, making difficult the storage of fat beneath the skin. To quote from Rodbard: "In small animals, the small amount of metabolizing mass compared to surface area available for heat loss results in a precarious juggling between the production of heat and its dissipation to the environment. This is manifested in the wide diurnal variations in body temperature seen in small birds. In the small mammals, with a less efficient insulation, a body temperature as high as that of the small birds apparently cannot be maintained. This is evidenced in the hypothermic response of small rodents to infection or to the injection of foreign proteins, which in larger animals leads to febrile response. This poorly developed homeothermism is also seen in the facility with which the body temperature of small mammals falls and a state of hibernation ensues on exposure to cold. By contrast, animals such as the bear with a large ratio of mass to surface area have only a slight fall in body temperature on entering the hibernating state."

The importance of insulation in adaptation, acclimatization, or acclimation to low external temperature is unquestioned and has long been recognized. There is a large literature on this subject, much of which also includes studies on heat-exchangers in the vascular system, metabolic adaptation under cold stress, and the adaptation in the melting points of fats in different parts of the body and in different climates, and changes in the conductivity of nerves. There seems little point in reviewing this literature here; it is all recent and new papers are constantly appearing, and it may be readily reached from the reference lists of such authors as Scholander (1955), Scholander, Hock, Walters, and Irving (1950), Scholander, Hock, Walters, Johnson, and Irving (1950), Scholander, Walters, Hock, and Irving (1950), and Burton and Edholm (1955). These publications deal with physiological and anatomical methods that have been evolved in association with problems of heat loss or heat gain, or of efficient functioning in cold climates, and they are peripheral to the subject of this book.

Chapter 3
THE PLEISTOCENE EVENT

It is both remarkable and intriguing that "no one to date has been quite able satisfactorily to account for that series of rhythmic and over-whelming catastrophes which we call the Ice Age. It is true that we no longer cloak such mysteries in an aura of supernaturalism, but they continue to remind us, nevertheless, of the latent forces still lurking within nature" (Eiseley 1963). There is much controversy even on such general matters as the time of onset of the first glaciation of the Pleistocene and upon its nature, that is, whether it was a relatively sudden event or whether the change was very gradual, involving time in hundreds of thousands or in millions of years. One point at least raises little argument: We are still in the Pleistocene epoch. The term "recent," so far as it might give the impression of a period different in some essential way from the Pleistocene or Quaternary, is misleading. Glaciation still exists in the world at both poles, in Antarctica and Greenland, probably even to much the same extent (thickness) as in the true glacial (as opposed to inter-glacial) periods in those regions.

There is, however, some doubt about where in the Pleistocene climatic progression we lie at present. Some authorities lean to the view that we are at the moment "approximately two-thirds of the way from the glacial to the interglacial extreme" (Willett 1953), that is to say that we have not yet reached the full climatic maximum (peak of warm climate). On the other hand, there is some evidence which suggests (it does no more) that the maximum has been passed, and that we are gradually returning to another glaciation. This is a possible implication of the analysis by Wiseman (1954) of the Foraminiferan fauna and the amount of carbonate in Foraminiferan skeletons in deep-sea sediment cores (Fig. 6) at different levels. In warmer water, more carbonate is deposited in the skeletons than in cold, so that the quantity of CO_2 that can be obtained from them gives a measure of the relative temperature of the water in which the organisms lived. The climatic maximum about 5000–6000 years ago agrees with the findings from other sources of information, and the shape of the curve as a whole strongly suggests that it will not lose its symmetry by turning up again, except for the minor oscillations which it shows and which correspond to climatic fluctuations within historic time.

Much of the uncertainty on the question of whether the climate at the moment is becoming warmer or colder comes from the difficulty of

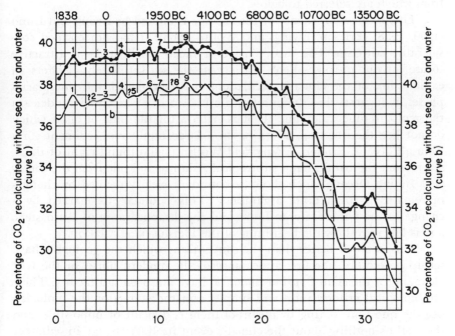

FIG. 6 Carbon dioxide measurements from sediment core taken in the Equatorial Atlantic, 01°10'N, 19°50'W, depth ca. 4350 m, by the Swedish "Albatross" Expedition. Redrawn from Wiseman (1954).

distinguishing the period of the particular oscillation we are studying. Climatic oscillations occur all the time, in periods ranging from a few years to centuries, millennia, and millions of years. Wiseman's evidence from the sea floor shows a decisive and sustained cooling over the past 6000 years, but the general trend contains oscillations of smaller interval up to the middle of the nineteenth century, which is as far as the curve goes, and we have ample evidence of two and perhaps three upswings in temperature since that time. The most recent, and also the most impressive in recent times, began about 1915 and came to its highest level in the 1940's approximately, and is very well documented (Jensen 1939, Dunbar 1946b); for general bibliography, see ICNAF (1953, 1965).

We have as yet no satisfactory theory of the causes of the first Pleistocene glaciation; each suggestion put forward meets with objections and counter-suggestions, and it is clear that the matter may not be settled for some time to come. There is no shortage of ideas, and recent years have seen the publication of several very useful symposia on the theme of climatic change in general and the Pleistocene event in particular, papers from which are referred to below.

The most recent theory of the Ice Age is offered by Ewing and Donn (1956, 1958) (Ericson, Ewing, and Wollin 1963); it has not escaped considerable criticism. The theory has four facets which make it attractive to use for our purposes here—it concerns the sea intimately, it offers an explanation of the climatic oscillations between glacial and interglacial phases, it suggests that the onset of the Pleistocene was rather sudden (in the geologic time-scale), and it offers criteria for the time of onset which do not beg the question. Working on a large number of sediment cores from all oceans, Ericson, Ewing, and Wollin (1963) found eight of them, seven from the tropical and subtropical Atlantic and one from the southwest Indian Ocean, which show "a boundary clearly defined by changes in remains of planktonic organisms." This boundary is marked by a change in the Foraminiferan fauna and the disappearance of Discoasters, and is taken to show the beginning of the Pleistocene glaciation.

This is much better than the conventions which the geologists have set up heretofore; the first appearance of the modern horse, or the true elephant, or the clam *Cyprina islandica,* have not been satisfactory. These are biological criteria pure and simple, and therefore (for the biologist) beg the question; dating by means of them is difficult or impossible, and they tell us nothing about the climatic event itself. A change in sediment fauna offers something that can be dated (although the dates chosen vary greatly), and which can give some indication of the rate of the climatic change; here too there are difficulties. Ericson, Ewing, and Wollin, in the paper quoted, set the date of the change at close to 800,000 years ago and estimated the duration of the process at less than 6000 years, perhaps much less.

Both in the dating and in the rate of change there is a great deal of controversy; even the same authors change their minds rapidly. The same three authors (Ericson, Ewing, and Wollin 1964) have brought forward evidence which might require us to extend the duration of the Pleistocene to 1,500,000 years, a suggestion which has been challenged. Damon (1965) has pointed out that the estimates of the length of the Pleistocene now range from 300,000 years (Emiliani 1955; Rosholt, Emiliani, Geiss, Koczy, and Wangersky 1961) to 1,500,000 years, and that furthermore the shortest and longest estimates "are based upon the same radiometric dates for deep-sea cores which were studied by both groups of workers." He concludes that we should "declare a moratorium on the construction of Pleistocene time scales until firmer data are available upon which to base such a chronology."

The decision on the duration of the Pleistocene is important for our present purpose. If the ecosystems of the high latitudes are to be interpreted as recently established and immature, the difference between the extremes of the present Pleistocene estimates is significant; but since the decision cannot be reached for the time being, we are forced to accept a Pleistocene of uncertain age and leave it at that.

One interesting feature of the Ewing-Donn theory of the origin of the glacial climate is that it does not call for extraterrestrial events, such as changes in the total energy received from the sun, or astronomical perturbations of the earth's axis and orbit, the density of cosmic dust, and so on. It requires the migration of the poles of the earth itself (for which there is considerable evidence from various sources) from former positions in free circulation oceanic bodies to the present positions: one pole in a large continental mass surrounded by oceans, the other in a contained ocean surrounded by land (Ewing and Donn 1964). This, to fill the requirements, must have occurred in the late Pliocene, and preferably fairly rapidly in geological terms. The Arctic Ocean, open and ice-free at the time of the arrival of the north pole in its centre, and in communication with the Atlantic Ocean (as now), provided the moisture source for the precipitation of snow necessary to form the ice sheets. As water became removed from the sea to the ice caps, the lowering of the sea level by a maximum of 150 metres (according to the most recent and liberal estimates) reduced the communication between the Atlantic and Arctic Oceans and thus cut down the supply of heat northward. This in turn resulted in the freezing over of the Arctic Ocean, and the consequent low precipitation allowed the summer melt to overcome the winter snow accumulation. The ice caps declined and with the return of water to the sea the cycle starts again.

This is the theory; it is ingenious and possibly the best we have at the moment, but there are certain objections which must be raised. The shallowest threshold across which the Atlantic water flows into the Arctic is the Wyville-Thompson Ridge between Scotland and Iceland, and to some extent also the continuation of the ridge west of Iceland in Denmark Strait. This ridge at present, in an interglacial period, is 500–600 metres deep; that is, its highest levels are about 500 metres below the surface. Allowing the greatest possible reduction in sea level at the height of the glacial periods to have been 150 metres, this still leaves 450 metres of depth for the Atlantic water to sweep north, which is not to be sneezed at. Furthermore, by far the largest amount of the heat carried by that water is in the upper 200 metres, and this transport would therefore not be affected by the fall in sea level.

It may be that there is a way to block that Atlantic inflow without bothering about the change in sea level; icebergs calved from the Greenland ice cap at present, which are the largest in the northern hemisphere, would not ground on a sill 450 metres deep, but the largest of the present Antarctic icebergs would do so, and it would be worth calculating whether icebergs of this size, calved from the Ungava and Greenland ice caps during glacial periods, would survive long enough in the Atlantic water to form a dam upon grounding on the Wyville-Thompson Ridge. Such a dam would be an effective brake upon the Atlantic inflow.*

The Pacific inflow, of course, through Bering Strait, was completely stopped during glacial periods, and this transport, smaller though it is than the Atlantic inflow to the Arctic, is not negligible, amounting to about a million cubic centimetres per second (one Sverdrup) on the average, and carrying a considerable amount of heat. This is a point in favour of the theory.

Another difficulty in the theory is that if it is correct, then either the Arctic Ocean should now be open or the warming towards the interglacial maximum still has a long way to go. The Arctic Ocean, however, is very far from being open, and, as already pointed out, the interglacial period in which we find ourselves appears to have reached or passed its maximum.

A totally different approach to the problem is required if the demands of some of the biogeographers (of the land fauna and flora) of the northwest Europe, Iceland and Greenland areas are to be met. Lindroth (1963), for instance, asks for a land connection from Greenland to Scotland, over Iceland, from some time in the Tertiary into at least the first interglacial period of the Pleistocene; Löve and Löve (1956) suggest that a Europe to Iceland bridge existed until the penultimate glaciation, and Sörenson (1953) asks for "late Pleistocene" as the date of the disappearance of the bridge. Others require the bridge to be present up to the end of the Pliocene, and still others ask for no bridge later than mid-Tertiary.

If a Scotland-Greenland land connection existed into the Pleistocene,

---

* In a third statement of the theory, Donn and Ewing (1966) have themselves eliminated the need for considering the change in sea level as important in the sequence of events; the change from glacier growth to glacier decay is accomplished by a small lowering of sea surface temperature, leading to reduction in precipitation.

then of course the Ewing-Donn theory will not work, because the supply of Atlantic water into the Arctic Ocean, and hence the necessary moisture for precipitation, would not have been available. On the other hand, the balance of scientific opinion at present is definitely not in favour of the bridge at all, possibly not at any time in the past; and furthermore if the world was sufficiently disturbed tectonically and isostatically to move the Wyville-Thompson Ridge up and down through some 1000 metres, it may well also have been prone to shift its poles at the same times, which would favour the first requirement of the present theory.

Other theories of the origin of the Pleistocene involve solar events and celestial mechanics which lie far outside the scope of this volume. They are covered in Fairbridge (1961). None has so far proved satisfactory, and we are therefore forced to admit that we are still some distance from an understanding of the Pleistocene causes, just as we are still quite uncertain when the event took place. Setting these two matters aside as temporarily unsolved, we are left with three parameters of the Pleistocene which are equally important in understanding polar ecology: the extent of the Pliocene-Pleistocene change, the rapidity with which it took place, and the amplitude of the glacial-interglacial oscillations. Here we are on slightly firmer ground, although two at least are still controversial.

The three points may best be treated together, and briefly. There is general agreement, based on changes in plant cover (pollen analysis) and the analysis of deep-sea sediment cores, that the climate of both land and sea cooled gradually from the Oligocene onward (see Dorf 1960 for general review). This cooling continued during the Pliocene. For the marine climate, Emiliani (1961 and elsewhere) agrees with this, and concludes that "surface temperatures in high latitudes, and bottom temperatures in all open oceanic basins decreased about 12°C during the past 75 million years." Fluctuations in Tertiary climate are also recognized, but agreement on them is not complete. For the land, van der Hammen (1961) records continuous fluctuations throughout the Tertiary, and a sudden drop in temperature (extent unspecified) at the beginning of the Quaternary. Emiliani (1961) finds that the marine sediment record shows fluctuations started about one million years ago, which on his time-scale is within the Pliocene, and the amplitude of the oscillation became greater at the Pleistocene beginnings; he is noncommittal about the extent of the Pliocene-Pleistocene change, but quotes Arrhenius (1952) as authority for a 3°C decrease in surface temperatures between the late Pliocene and the early Pleistocene, from analysis of Foraminifera.

Working from oxygen isotope analysis of deep-sea cores, Emiliani (1961) found that the surface temperatures during the Pleistocene itself oscillated within a range of 6 or 7°C in the equatorial Atlantic and about

12°C in the Mediterranean, and for the temperate and tropical seas as a whole, he shows a series of oscillations ranging from the high 20's to the low 20's (degrees Celsius) representing interglacial and glacial stages. In this scheme there are seven periods of low temperature within a total period of 300,000 years.

All this does not give the biologist a great deal to go on. We know that there was a significant climate change at the Pliocene-Pleistocene interphase, but we have little sure guidance in the extent of the change or in its rapidity. This is especially true of the Arctic, in which we are immediately interested. We may assume that the Arctic Ocean was open and unfrozen in pre-Pleistocene time, during all or most of the Tertiary; this at least is something. And if we accept the Ewing-Donn theory, we have a picture of an open Arctic Ocean during most of each glacial period, and of a frozen Arctic Ocean during most of each interglacial period; the extent of any lag effect that probably existed is uncertain. From evidence offered by Ericson (1959), Ewing and Donn (1960) have suggested that the surface temperatures of the Arctic Ocean during a glacial stage were between 0°C and 3.5°C. We may assume that we are at present in an interglacial, that is, that another glacial stage will follow unless mankind by that time can stop it.

We thus have two environmental systems, each offering pairs of contrasting conditions: the glacial-interglacial contrast, and the Pliocene-Pleistocene contrast. We know more about the former than the latter. We now have to ponder the effects of these two systems upon the biota of the polar regions.

One school of thought which is entirely at odds with all others has not yet been mentioned. This is the view put forward by Zenkevitch (1949) who bases his conclusions on estimates of endemism in the cold water marine fauna and states that the poverty of polar faunas (in species) can be explained not by lack of age, but only by lack of habitat diversity and by low temperature. Assuming certain lengths of time necessary for the evolution of marine species and genera, he concludes that polar cold water faunas have existed for several hundreds of millions of years, and that the present polar conditions are of similar great age. While admiring this bold and highly independent conclusion, biologists, paleontologists, and geologists have for the most part found it hard to accept in the face of other and contrary evidence. This matter is discussed again below in relation to the general problem of adaptation.

In a recent paper on the phylogeny of the Caspian and Baikal seals, McLaren (1960) comes to the conclusion that the subfamily Phocinae was evolved by the late Miocene at the latest, and that they were at that time Arctic forms adapted to life on ice; he therefore favours considerable cooling in the late Tertiary, in agreement with Barghoorn (1953), whom he quotes: "the great trend of Cenozoic climate which culminated in Pleistocene glaciation began in the mid-Tertiary, probably more than 20 million years ago. Pleistocene glaciation itself . . . may then be regarded as a geologic and climatologic event the antecedents of which extend over a fair segment of recent geologic time and is not to be viewed as a sudden change in the history of the earth's climate."

Chapter 4

ENVIRONMENT AND PRODUCTION
IN POLAR REGIONS

In a textbook on Arctic adaptations, or on the polar regions as such, it would be necessary for completeness to deal in a detailed manner with polar environments offered to living creatures on land, in lakes, and in the sea. This is not the intention here. We all know that the higher latitudes receive much less direct solar energy than do the temperate and polar regions, and that the processes of life in general are at a lower level, as regards the variety of species and growth rates, than in warmer regions. The particular matter of the variety of species, or the complexity of the ecosystem, is considered in Chapters 5, 6, and 8. It is necessary here, however, to point out certain aspects of the high latitude environments which affect the present study, especially the differences in production found in different parts, and their causes, and the high degree of seasonal oscillation which is characteristic of the polar regions, in strong contrast to the tropics.

The living systems of the world obtain their energy ultimately from the sun, and this solar energy, as it comes to earth, has a symmetrical pattern of distribution in the atmosphere; the distribution on the surface of the earth itself is sophisticated by cloud cover and other climatic effects which are variable from season to season and from year to year. Solar energy (heat) is lost from the global system in back radiation from the earth, part of which is not trapped in the atmosphere, and in radiation from the atmosphere, especially in high latitudes. There is a net gain in solar energy at the equator and a net loss in the polar regions, which is balanced by transport of heat polewards both in the atmosphere and in the hydrosphere.

We are dealing here with energy in the forms of (1) heat and (2) light, (3) as a process of motion (kinetic energy), and (4) as chemical energy summed as potential and kinetic energy; by this latter is meant energy contained in chemical substances in the biological cycle (Fig. 7) or in process of being transferred in chemical reactions. The energy contained in chemical substances is regarded as potential energy, including the energy content of substances in deep stable water, and in deep soils, whose return to active regions may involve a long time. Presumably potential energy, stored as nutrient salts (plant nutrients),* may lie out of reach for very long periods in deep stable water; Ferguson Wood's (1965) statement that "bursts of productivity in past centuries could account for the animal populations of today" can be expanded to include plant populations as well. The fact is, of course, that both heat and potential chemical

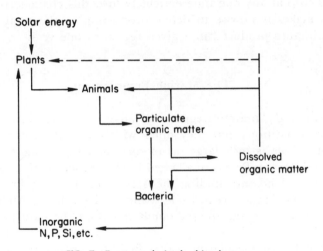

FIG. 7 Energy cycle in the biosphere.

energy can readily be transported in space, and chemical energy can readily be transported in time as well, so that the distribution of energy in the total system is four-dimensional and involves much movement. The inclusion of climatic change extends the time-scale even further.

The central question to be discussed concerns the forms of energy whose availability is limiting to production, but before doing this it is

---

* This, of course, is to go beyond what is normally allowed to be the meaning of the term "energy." There is need for some new term, such as "biocapacity" or "biopotential," which when used together with the orthodox sense of "energy" would include all that is involved in the determination of a bioproductive system. Lacking such a term for the moment, this misuse of "energy" seems reasonable. "Matter" and "energy" after all, are now, even in elementary textbooks, considered to be different forms of the same thing; the problem remaining is to decide what that "thing" is to be called within the framework of the present discussion. This applies also to the discussion below of "energy flow" and "energy storage" (see, e.g., page 64).

necessary to define what sort of production or productivity we are talking about. The definition of "productivity," "production," and other related terms is becoming rather tiresome in the literature, but there is no doubt that precision is necessary. I am going to use one term only here—*production*—defined as the standing crop per unit area, averaged per shorter time unit over the year. This sums all shorter events, skids over the matter of the *rate* of production, and has the merit of giving a measure of the economic value of different parts of the world in the supply of food. It also evades the almost metaphysical difficulty of deciding what to do with stable tropical waters in which energy turnover can be rapid but the standing crop at any one time extremely low; this characteristic of tropical seas makes it unwise to define production as the total amount of living substance produced in a given region in one year.

The Marine Environment

The Arctic and Antarctic regions are alike in general physical and atmospheric conditions, but they differ widely in almost everything else. The North Pole is in a large ocean surrounded on almost all sides by land, and the South Pole is in a large island continent entirely surrounded by water; the land surrounding the Arctic Ocean is very low in productivity, as is the Arctic Ocean itself, while the land of the Antarctic is entirely covered by ice and the surrounding seas are the most productive in the world.

To deal with the marine aspect first: It is generally accepted that three external factors are basic to primary production (the growth of plants). There is a minimum temperature requirement, there must be light, and there must be a supply of inorganic nutrients (nitrates, phosphates, silicates, etc.), and any one of these, if it is in short supply, can be limiting. In the normal situation in nature, however, it appears that the first two factors are not limiting in marine production anywhere in the world, including the high latitudes, in terms of the annual cycle (there are obviously times, such as the Arctic winter, when light is effectively limiting), but that low temperatures may limit the *rate* at which primary production continues at any given time. It has been made clear in Chapter 2 that animals can and do regulate their metabolism and activity with respect to temperature, but that growth is usually slowed down, and although there seems to have been very little work done on this aspect of plant production, it is possible that for aquatic plants at least the same will be found to hold good. The seasonal temperature oscillation in the air is so much greater than in water that the land plants must be considered separately.

Although such a growth rate effect in cold water may slow down the process of primary production to some extent, it does not stop it, even in extreme Arctic or Antarctic temperatures of $-1.7°C$ or lower. Indeed, it is remarkable how rapidly the spring phytoplankton develops in the Arctic, where the change from extreme clarity of water to thick green turbidity occurs within a very few days. At all events, the evidence already presented shows that the low polar temperatures are not limiting, and that the geography of marine production has no correlation with temperatures (Fig. 8). At the other end of the temperature range this becomes equally clear; large areas of tropical waters are very low in productivity, and yet high production in the tropics is found where the right conditions exist.

So far as is known, most marine plant growth stops completely during the Arctic and Antarctic winter, and appears to do so also in the middle latitudes; this effect is normally attributed to lack of light. But in assessing the total annual production in any part of the world, it is clear that the lack of light during the year as a whole is not a limiting factor, except possibly in the Arctic Ocean itself, and even here it is doubtful. The light available during the polar summer is in large supply, and moreover there is now evidence that certain algae of the high latitudes are adapted to much lower light intensities than are those of other regions (see below).

We are thus left with the supply of nutrients as the decisive factor in determining the annual production of phytoplankton in different parts of the world, and hence the production as a whole. The nutrient salts must be available in the euphotic zone in the surface waters, and since they are formed by the bacterial oxidation of organic detritus which sinks down toward the bottom, the supply to the surface waters depends upon physical upward transport of this deeper water, either by vertical exchange during the winter, which is characteristic of temperate regions, or by some other advective process. This is the process vividly described by Sverdrup as "deep ploughing."

Vertical exchange of water due to winter cooling of the surface layers, normal in temperate regions, is not found in the tropics because the surface water does not cool sufficiently to give the necessary density change. It does not seem to occur in many high Arctic situations either, owing to the maintenance of low surface density by the meltwater of ice. Arctic waters usually become highly stable during the early spring owing to the melting of ice and glacial runoff from the land, a phenomenon which was mentioned in Chapter 2 in relation to the rapid growth of certain planktonic larval forms, but the winter conditions have not been given much attention. Hudson Bay, which develops an upper layer during the spring and summer of very low density, seems nevertheless to form

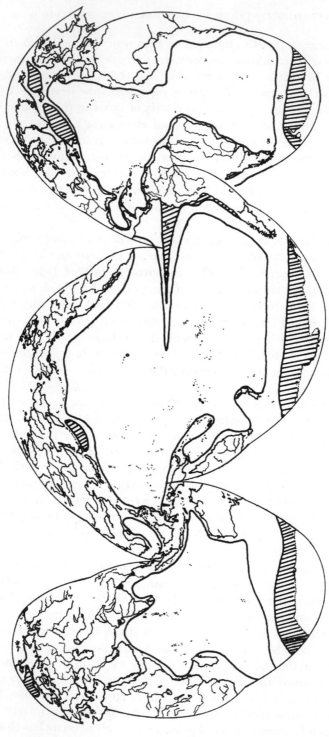

FIG. 8 World map of marine production, after Sverdrup (1955). The most productive areas are crosshatched; the next most productive areas lie shoreward of the solid line.

a fairly uniform density column from surface to bottom in the winter, on the evidence of one station (Dunbar 1958). From the Beaufort Sea area of the Arctic Ocean, Kusunoki (1962) has recorded density profiles for the year 1959–60. At all times of year the water is stable, except for small instabilities in the upper 10 metres in the late winter (February to May). The water column in the upper 50 metres is frequently close to being homopycnic except during the summer and fall (June to November), when it is stable; but at no time of year does the upper 200-metre column taken as a whole approach instability, for it is always highly stratified. Timofeyev (1960) found the depth of the convection on the Atlantic side of the Lomonosov Ridge (Eurasian Basin) of the Arctic Ocean to be only 40–45 metres, and about 75 metres or less on the Pacific side (Canada Basin).

It is clear that the Arctic Ocean as a whole is vertically very stable at all times of year. Since light and temperature are not likely to be limiting in the annual production, the low production of the Arctic Ocean may reasonably be put down to this stability. The nutrients themselves are there in normal and adequate quantities (Kusunoki 1962, together with Russian data), but they do not reach the euphotic zone in sufficient quantity; very probably they are slowly accumulating in the deeper layers.

In productivity and in vertical stability the Arctic Ocean stands in great contrast to the waters of the Antarctic; a comparison of the two is instructive. Figure 9 shows the effect of the Antarctic ice cap on the movement of the water surrounding it. Meltwater of low density flows to the north, creating a significant surface current. Water cooled by the ice sinks down the shelf and slope. Both of these cause replacement effects, and the replacement comes mainly from below, bringing to the surface nutrient-rich deep water. The wind aids and abets this upwelling. The westerlies which blow round the world in those latitudes (north of the Antarctic Divergence, south of which there are coastal easterly winds) cause a movement of surface water away from the Divergence, owing to the left-handed effect of the Coriolis factor, thereby increasing the upwelling from below. These two systems thus combine to raise the production in Antarctic waters and to keep it at a high level, and it seems that this condition is maintained through much of the year; El-Sayed et al. (1964), for instance, found the phosphate content of the surface water in Drake Passage in March (late summer) to be 2 μg atom/1, which is high for that time of the biological year in other parts of the world.

No such conditions exist in the Arctic, except (in part and locally) at the sea-faces of glaciers in Greenland and in Spitsbergen, where small regions of upwelling exist (Stott 1936; Hartley and Dunbar 1938); such local zones are of little overall significance. But the north does have an important characteristic which is far less developed in the south, namely a broad zone in which Arctic and non-Arctic water are found together in the upper layers (200–300 metres), either in closely associated streams or as mixed water. The Antarctic Convergence is a narrow front zone, in which the densities of the two water masses concerned are distinct and discourage mixing. The Arctic Convergence is far more diffuse: by the time the Atlantic Drift water reaches Newfoundland and the region south

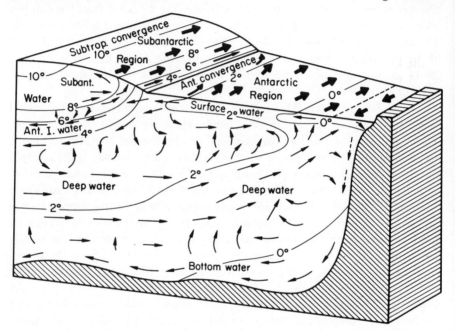

FIG. 9   Block diagram of currents and water masses of the Antarctic, from Sverdrup, Johnson, and Fleming (1946); redrawn with permission of the publishers.

of Greenland, it has cooled to a point such that its density, allowing for the difference in salinities between the Arctic and Atlantic water, is close to that of the Arctic water itself; this results in ready mixing and apparently also, in certain instances at least, in cabbeling * (Smith, Soule, and Mosby 1937). When the Drift water has reached as far north as Spitsbergen, further cooling has increased its density to well above that of the

* *Cabbeling* is the phenomenon of the mixing of two water masses of equal density but of differing temperature and salinity which, at certain values of these two parameters, may result in the production of a mixed water of greater density than either of its original components.

Arctic water, which is also less saline, so that at that part of the front it sinks beneath the upper Arctic water; this is the reverse of the pattern at the Antarctic Convergence.

There is thus established in the area from Newfoundland to the Barents Sea a broad zone in which Atlantic water penetrates to the north and Arctic water penetrates to the south, in the upper two or three hundred metres, and in which there is a great deal of mixing. (This should be distinguished from those areas, such as Denmark Strait, in which Arctic water in deeper layers spills over the Wyville-Thompson Ridge into the deep Atlantic.) Mixing on this scale tends toward uniform density in the water column and hence to instability and increased production. Hence the zone of mixing, which has been defined as the marine Subarctic * (Dunbar 1954 and elsewhere), differs markedly from the Arctic zone to the north of it, and is of great importance economically since many of the important fisheries of the northern hemisphere are found in it. Its approximate extent is illustrated in Fig. 10. A similar zone, but considerably smaller, is found on the Pacific side, north of Alaska, in the Chukchi Sea, and to some extent also in the Bering Sea, but the effect on the Pacific side is far less than in the North Atlantic.

There is now a considerable literature on the characteristics of this marine Subarctic. For our present purposes the important points about it are these:

1. Higher temperatures than in the Arctic, which may be illustrated by comparing conditions in Godthaab Fjord or the southwest Greenland coast generally with those of Foxe Basin or the Arctic Ocean. Excluding the upper 50–100 metres which are variable and affected by short-term and local influences, the Arctic zone water remains well below zero throughout the year, and for most of the year is close to the freezing point at $-1.7°C$, whereas temperatures in southwest Greenland are normally positive, and usually above $2°C$, even in winter. The pattern of distribution of temperatures at the 200-metre level (Schroeder 1963) is also instructive.

* The terms "Subarctic" and "Subantarctic" as applied to the marine environment are not at present used consistently. As used here, *Subarctic* refers to the region with mixed Arctic and non-Arctic water in the upper 200 to 300 metres. *Pacific Subarctic* as used by Sverdrup, Johnson, and Fleming (1946) refers to the waters of the North Pacific in the Gulf of Alaska region, which contain no Arctic water at all; the *Subantarctic* is usually understood to mean the broad zone between the Antarctic Convergence and the Subtropical Convergence to the north, which is innocent of any Antarctic water in the upper layers.

FIG. 10 The Subarctic regions of the world, land and sea. The Subarctic of the land (crosshatched) follows Kimble and Good (1955); the Subarctic of the sea (stippled) follows Dunbar (1954).

2. Lesser vertical stability both in summer and winter. Table 1 gives stability values during the late summer and winter in the Godthaab Fjord region, compared with Kusunoki's (1962) stabilities for the Arctic Ocean. This lesser stability makes possible, in the Subarctic, a second phytoplankton bloom in the autumn (as in temperate waters), in contrast with the single cycle of events in Arctic water. Compare the events recorded by Bursa (1961) during one year in northern Foxe Basin (Fig. 11) with the prolonged and two-peak phytoplankton production recorded by Nielsen (1958) in Godthaab Fjord, west Greenland (Fig. 12).

TABLE 1 Vertical stability for winter stations 17 and 18, Ice Island T-3, February–March, 1960 (Kusunoki 1962); and for Godthaab Fjord, West Greenland, Station 1 (mouth of fjord) and Station 13 (head of fjord) January 1946 (Dunbar 1951).

	T-3	Godthaab Fjord	
		St. 13	St. 1
Depth (m)	$10^5 (d\sigma_t/dz)$ *		
0			
	−45	−600	1600
10			
	2230	653	560
50			
	4160	0	160
100			
	2350	280	360
200			

* Where σ_t = density of water in *situ*

z = depth of water layer in metres.

The values given are a measure of the stabilities between the given depths, being the results of dividing the density difference by the differences in depth.

3. Less ice cover. The Subarctic zone is almost entirely free of ice in summer, except for adventitious floes and bergs, and the greater portion is ice-free also in winter.

4. Greater variety of fauna and flora (greater ecosystem complexity). This is shown in all taxonomic groups, in which the number of species found in the Subarctic is several times the number for the Arctic. See for instance, for amphipod crustacea, Dunbar (1954); for copepods, Fontaine (1955); and for fishes, Hildebrand (n.d. and 1948).

5. Greater organic production as already implied above. Figures for primary production are now available for both the Arctic and Subarctic zones, but since they are *rates*, expressed usually as amounts of carbon assimilated per day, they do not help us much in the total estimation of the production in any given region; there are so many variables involved that even rough approximation is impossible. For zooplankton, measured quantitatively, we are still short of good data, but there is no doubt of the general richness of the Subarctic in this respect. The most impressive index is the fishery production, which in the Arctic zone is nil; Subarctic fisheries, on the other hand, include the enormous productions of the Newfoundland Grand Banks, the Labrador coast, west Greenland, north-

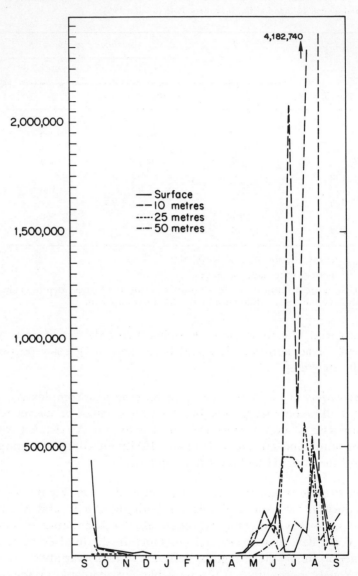

FIG. 11 Phytoplankton population at Igloolik, northern Foxe Basin, 1955–56, expressed as numbers of cells per litre. Redrawn from Bursa (1961).

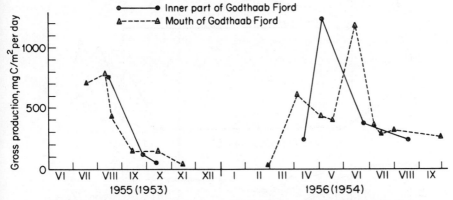

FIG. 12 Gross primary production in Godthaab Fjord, west Greenland. The inner fjord, more Arctic in type than the mouth, shows a shorter productive period. Redrawn from Steemann Nielsen (1958).

ern Iceland (perhaps all of Iceland should be included), and much of the Barents Sea.

6. Lesser seasonal oscillation, both in standing crop and in most environmental factors. The lesser environmental oscillation follows from the lesser ice cover and from the generally more southerly position. There are of course modifications to be made to this statement; Hudson Bay (Arctic) is considerably further south than southwest Spitsbergen waters (Subarctic), and indeed both areas are special, each in its own way. Also the Arctic zone no doubt varies less in temperature seasonally than does the Subarctic. But in the important matter of the contrast between the season of production and the season of overwintering, or dormancy, in the seasonal changes in light conditions, and in the standing crop in winter, this difference stands. The season of plankton breeding and growth is very short in the Arctic, and the hazards of the long nonproductive period are great; the effect of this on the evolution of Arctic biota and ecosystems is discussed in Chapter 6. The short and sudden period of production in Arctic regions is nowhere better illustrated than in Grainger's (1959) study of the annual cycle in northern Foxe Basin (Fig. 13). Notice that even the phosphate concentrations at the bottom (50 metres) remain extremely low all winter, which might suggest that the bacteria responsible for the phosphate regeneration do not regulate their metabolism to the low temperature, but rather follow the Van't Hoff rule.

7. Greater sensitivity to marine climatic change. Climatic changes in the sea appear to be caused by change in the heat absorbed by surface waters

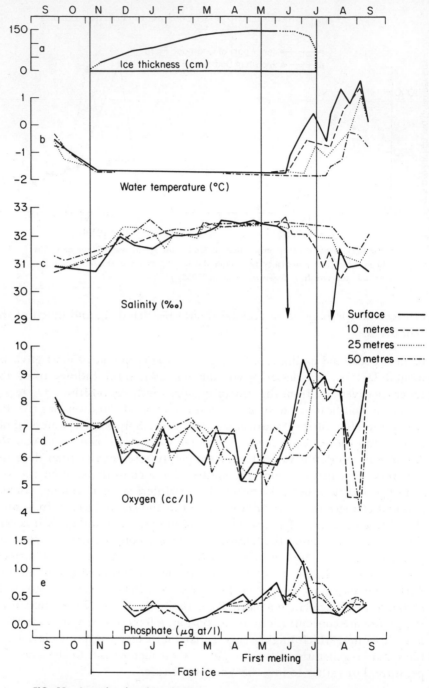

FIG. 13 Annual cycles of ice thickness, temperature, salinity, dissolved oxygen, and dissolved inorganic phosphate, at Igloolik, northern Foxe Basin, 1955–56. From Grainger (1959).

48

in tropical and subtropical regions and by changes in the proportions of the component parts of the waters of any given region. Thus the recent climatic warming, which seems to have been worldwide, was manifested in the Atlantic-Arctic area in a greater intensity of circulation of the Gulf Stream system and an increase in the heat transported by it. The Subarctic areas, such as west Greenland and northern Iceland, responded immediately to these changes, whereas the Arctic Ocean and its outflows in east Greenland and the Canadian Archipelago appeared to have been affected not at all, or very slightly.

A marine subpolar zone of this nature is absent from the Antarctic, where the whole hydrographic situation is entirely different. Furthermore, it is doubtful whether any part of the Subarctic, productive as it is, can equal the Antarctic in the amount of living stuff produced. Precise measurements on this matter are still lacking, but at least it is quite clear that, in comparing the Arctic zone with the Antarctic, which two zones show so many faunal and ecological similarities, those similarities cannot be referred to the effects of the level of production upon the system. This is an important point, as will be developed later, because it eliminates one basic set of possible reasons for the nature of polar ecosystems, leaving perhaps only the seasonal oscillation, which is far less in the Antarctic, and the matter of the age or maturity of the ecosystem itself, an effect of time.

The global "geography of marine production" is well shown in Sverdrup's (1955) map, Fig. 8. Notice that the regions of high production do not follow latitude or temperature as already mentioned; they occur in all major regions of the world except the Arctic, and the crucial factor in determining their distribution is the vertical stability of the water. The reasons for instability off the west coast of South America and in the equatorial Pacific are those of wind and Coriolis effect, and have not been discussed here.

Before leaving the matter of the productivity of the polar regions, attention should be drawn to a special sort of primary production, forming the basis of a special and localized ecosystem, which exists on the under surface of sea ice in both the Arctic and the Antarctic. Apollonio (1961) in the Arctic (Jones Sound), and Meguro (1962), Bunt (1963), and Bunt and Wood (1963) in the Antarctic, have described and measured this algal growth, which begins to appear at some unspecified time during the late winter or early spring and disappears as the snow and ice melt; the production takes place before the normal planktonic plant production and the plants concerned are adapted to extraordinarily low light intensities. The chlorophyll a to chlorophyll c ratio is low compared with the normal; chlorophyll c is about six times as efficient as chlorophyll a in absorbing blue light. This flora is of considerable intrinsic interest, and furthermore it represents, according to Apollonio's calculations, a standing crop of considerable size for a period of some two months; it forms food, during that time, for a crustacean grazing population. Apart from the question of the biochemical adaptations shown by this flora, there is also a problem to be solved in the manner in which this population is recruited each year, of the source of reinoculation of the ice. The problem is no doubt mainly taxonomic, a question of which of the surface phytoplankters form the ice flora.

Finally, what we know of the bottom fauna of the two polar regions shows that the Antarctic benthos is a great deal richer, probably in variety and certainly in biomass, than its counterpart in the Arctic Ocean. This is to be expected since the quantity of benthos reflects the total productivity of the water and is not so sensitive to seasonal oscillations as is the plankton.

The Environment of the Land

With the exception of the southern tip of South America, the extent of high latitude terrestrial environment is restricted to the northern hemisphere. The Antarctic continent, covered with ice, in fact represents the condition of large areas in the north during Pleistocene glaciations, and there is little doubt that the Antarctic ice cap has been continuous and uninterrupted since at least the beginning of the Pleistocene.

The Arctic and Subarctic marine conditions during glacial times, as opposed to the present interglacial situation, are not at all clear, as has been indicated above; the conditions on land, however, are well understood at least in outline. There may be controversy about how many glaciations have occurred, and even on the precise geographic coverage of the glaciations, but there is no argument on the general pattern, both in time and space. Ice caps which entirely obliterated the land have waxed and waned during Pleistocene time over the whole of Canada and Alaska (with the exception of the Alaskan north and west and possibly certain island areas in northern Canada), and over northwest Europe and parts of Siberia, with the important result that on the land, even more than in the sea, the time which the present plant and animal populations of the north have had to become established and ecologically balanced is quite short, of the order of 3000 to 15,000 years, depending on the region, and that this is all the time that has been available for the soil, the basis of terrestrial ecosystems, to form from bare rock over very large areas of territory.

Regions formerly glaciated in North America are now covered by mixed woods, conifer forest, steppe (as in the western prairies), taiga and various muskegs, tundra, and residual ice caps. The same pattern may be seen in Eurasia, but the northern Asian condition differs in the one important fact that most of the land was not glaciated, and hence the soils are of longer establishment. Northern climates are climates of extremes, especially in the Subarctic areas, and the winters are not hospitable to many species of animals, with the consequence that migration and various types of dormancy are very common. Except for these two climatic characteristics, however, the Arctic and Subarctic of the land are closely comparable with their equivalents in the sea, in matters of ecosystem complexity, low temperature, light conditions, and productivity; even in the weather there are the same seasonal environmental oscillations —they are simply more violent on land.

Quantitative production studies in the north, which are only just beginning in marine research, are even less advanced in terrestrial environments, although the general study of the latter is older. The scientific literature is considerable, from such excellent earlier accounts as that of Haviland (1926), through a great mass of botanical and zoological work in the 1930's, to the more specialized attacks of the postwar years. A good general account of terrestrial Arctic ecology has been published by Dansereau (1955), and a more detailed analysis, with special reference to the insects, is offered by Downes (1964). By way of introduction to the subject, and to emphasize the difference between Arctic and Antarctic, here is a vivid passage from Downes:

"Things being as they are the Arctic land areas have a cold winter that is succeeded by a summer warm enough and long enough to permit the development of an interesting flora and fauna. North of the 75th parallel, in the northern Canadian islands alone, there are some 150 species of vascular plants and perhaps 300 species of insects (exclusive of Collembola) representing nine orders. But how different it might have been. In the Antarctic the only true insects that have been collected south of the 75th parallel are a very few species of lice parasitic on birds and seals; and in all Antarctica, which extends to 63°S at one point, the total insect fauna other than lice consists of two species of Chironomidae . . . and one flea that breeds in the nests of sea birds . . . ."

Various delimitations of the Arctic from the Subarctic zones, and the Subarctic from the Temperate, have been suggested for the environments of the land. Kimble and Good (1955) and others have chosen the July 50° isotherm as the southern limit of the Arctic, which has the merit of close agreement with the limit of trees; the limit of trees itself is perhaps the simplest and most sensible criterion to choose. The southern limit of the Subarctic we can take as the southern limit of the full boreal forest, or conifer forest lying to the north of the mixed woods of the Transition. These lines of delimitation are shown in Fig. 10, and should be compared and contrasted with the pattern for the marine environment; there is little correspondence between the two systems.

In this Land of the Long Day, which is also the Land of the Long Night, the sun is above the horizon continuously in summer for many days—at Lake Hazen, latitude 81°49′N, from April 11 to August 31, or 143 days (Downes 1964). It is often mistakenly believed that this implies continuous intensity of light during the 24-hour period, which is by no means the case. At latitude 80°, for instance, in clear weather, the radiation received by a unit area of surface is about three times as great at noon as it is at midnight. This is very important when considering diurnal rhythms in living organisms in the Arctic; there is plenty of evidence for the continuance of such circadian behaviour in the polar summer. Rhythmic behaviour in the Arctic winter does not appear to have been examined.

The heat budget is small, and the growing season short; to both of which characteristics the land flora and fauna of the north have adapted in much the same way as has already been described for marine animals. To quote Downes (1964) again: "it seems to be a characteristic of many organisms in the Arctic that they are able to grow and carry on their activities at lower temperatures than their southern counterparts." Metabolic regulation with respect to temperature is shown, for example, by many insects, which are able to maintain flight and other locomotor activities at temperatures close to zero. Bertram (1935) was among the first to study this phenomenon, and it has been suggested by Salt (1961) that the adaptation is essentially one of changes in the enzyme systems involved. Growth rates are low in both plants and poikilothermous animals, and insects may take several years to reach maturity, overwintering in a variety of growth stages.

Over the whole of the Arctic zone on land, and in patchy distribution in the northern part of the Subarctic, permafrost is found. Although permafrost may have an effect upon the rate of soil formation, its ecological significance otherwise is still uncertain, except as it affects soil drainage; it is not a matter that affects the present discussion.

Bliss (1962) states that "of the various environmental factors temperature is the most important limiting factor with regard to plant growth and development in the tundra," and goes on to suggest that small size in Arctic plants may be an advantage, rather than a necessary result of slow growth, in making use of the warmer microclimates that exist near the soil in summer. Since plants have no locomotor problems on land, and therefore no need to regulate "activity" in the animal sense with respect to low temperatures, this direct dependence on temperature is to be expected; it is in fact tantamount to saying that the growth rates of plants are slowed down by low temperature just as they are in poikilothermous animals. There is no call, at the ultimate level, for metabolic regulation. Nevertheless the naming of temperature as the limiting factor in the development of tundra plant cover seems unwise, in view of the little we know as yet of Arctic soils, and of the nutrient supply, both of which must be thought to have equally good *a priori* claims to this distinction. Controversy on this subject in fact exists [again, see Bliss (1962, p. 133)].

In the matter of nutrient supply, the land and the sea stand, as it were, at opposite ends of a conveyor system; there is a constant drain, or leaching out, of nutrients from the land to the sea, by way of rivers and land drainage in general, so that the problem of what determines the geography of production on land is not quite so simple as it appears to be in the sea. The sea has an enormous and ever-growing capital of plant nutrients; the land has a capital of nutrients which it must keep in as high a steady-state balance as it can, with constant production (by mineralization of organic matter and new production from the lithosphere) and constant loss (by drainage to the sea). The feedback from the sea to the land is probably negligible, consisting of the products of migrant bird populations and the like, apart of course from the activities of man in certain areas.

The amount of soil present, which can hold nutrients in solution by capillary action, and particularly humus soil, is obviously an important factor here, and it is precisely in soil that the Arctic terrestrial environment is so poor. There is thus a good case to be made for the view that the availability of nutrients may be as important as, or more important than, temperature, in determining the relative primary productivity of land areas, as it is in the sea. It suggests also that the most hopeful practical advance in improving Arctic land productivity might be the discovery of a means of significantly accelerating the process of soil formation from rock.

However that may be, it is established that the Arctic lands rate very low in productivity. Estimates for tundra production range from 0.2 to 0.6 $g/m^2/day$, averaged over the whole year (total dry weight), which amounts to about one-fifth of the production for good temperate woodland (Downes 1964). The terrestrial Arctic (tundra) is more productive, relative to temperate regions, than is the Arctic Ocean compared with Subarctic or temperate seas. The tundra in fact appears to be comparable to the peripheral Arctic marine areas in this respect; but the factors which determine the geographic differences on land are likely to be more complex and are certainly less well understood. Extreme regions of the high Arctic on land, the so-called "feldmark" regions, produce much less than the tundra proper, the lowest figures being of the order of $0.01g/m^2/day$, total dry weight, based on the whole year, or about two per cent of good tundra production. It is very interesting to find that this agrees remarkably well with the marine figures; English (1961) records an annual carbon fixation in the Arctic Ocean amounting to less than one-hundredth that of the Sargasso Sea, or about two per cent of the production in Jones Sound, a peripheral Arctic area which corresponds to the tundra, as just suggested.

Bliss (1962) makes the interesting point that tundra plants are "amazingly efficient with regard to energy conversion," when compared with temperate vegetation. That is, the daily increment during the growing season is of the same order in the tundra as it is in numerous temperate plant communities. This is precisely the phenomenon, shown in plants, which Wohlschlag (1960) speculated might exist in Antarctic fishes, as mentioned in Chapter 2 above.

Lakes

"Over half of the birds of the tundra are aquatic or littoral" (Haviland 1926). All of these are migrants, and many of them feed on the summer fauna and flora or freshwater bodies, which indicates that the productivity of tundra ponds and lakes is not negligible. Shallow ponds can in fact produce quite remarkable crops of insect larvae and small Crustacea, sometimes also sticklebacks, with a corresponding supporting flora; and the number of such small bodies of freshwater in the north is very large. Arctic lakes in general, however, are extremely oligotrophic, and for good and proper reasons.

The productivity of lakes is determined by depth, climate, and nutrient capital, the latter being in turn determined by age and the geological and botanical properties of the surrounding land. Shallower lakes tend to be more productive than deep lakes because of the greater ease of mixing and hence return of nutrients to the surface. More important than depth, however, are climate and age, and in both categories Arctic lakes are at a disadvantage compared with lakes in temperate regions. Surface temperatures in many years do not rise above the 4°C point of maximum density. This would under normal circumstances, with the bottom water at 4°C, discourage vertical mixing at any time of year, but in fact the bottom water itself is often below the 4°C point in the north, so that mixing can occur during the open water period under the influence of even a slight wind, and there is usually very little (if any) establishment of a thermocline, especially in the deeper lakes. The open water period, however, is extremely short, and in some cases and in some years the ice cover does not disappear at all.

The decisive determinant is the supply of mineral nutrients, which is very small in Arctic lakes. To quote Oliver's (1964) study of Nettilling Lake in Baffin Island: "This scarcity of minerals is considered as an indication of low productive capacity. Northcote and Larkin (1956) found there was a better correlation of productivity with total solids than with any other single factor. Rawson (1958) also emphasizes this correlation." This lack of minerals is a function of age, or the lack of it; it is related to the youth of the landscape since the retreat of the ice, and the corresponding poverty of soil and plant cover. As the nutrient capital grows in northern lakes, the production will rise; it is a "bootstraps" operation, as the gradual growth of all productivity has been, land, sea, and freshwater, through geological time.

Chapter 5

ECOLOGICAL ADAPTATION AND EVOLUTION (I)

Whatever the details of the "Pleistocene event," the beginning of the Ice Age, about which there is so much controversy, there is little argument on the fact of a very large environmental change. Whether the change came rapidly or slowly, in terms of temperature, is perhaps not the most significant matter, since it is apparent (Chapter 2) that adaptation to low temperature as such presents few evolutionary difficulties and has been accomplished by thousands of species. What is important is the manner in which other environmental conditions changed, in particular seasonal oscillation of productivity and light conditions, and (on land) erosion of the whole substrate of life by the ice itself.

Whether these changes took place as the effects of the shifting of the poles from positions in freely circulating world oceans (North Pacific and South Atlantic) or whether as a result of a change in the total energy received from the sun is not yet clear; evidence is in favour of the polar shift. Our concern is the manner in which the communities of organisms responded to these changes, to give the ecological situation we find in the high latitudes today.

The question touches also the fauna of the deep seas, in that by the onset of the Pleistocene the deep water of the oceans had dropped some 12°C in temperature. There is a sharp division of opinion on this, and on the age of the abyssal fauna. Bruun and Wolff (1961) have maintained that the composition of the deep fauna indicates a recent origin, and point to the temperature drop as the reason for this, the decline in temperature having extinguished most of the supposed former population. Zenkevitch (1961) on the other hand, analyzing the same fauna, considers that the deep oceanic fauna of the whole world is very ancient.

It is typical of biogeographic studies that the same data can be, and are, interpreted as indicating quite different histories by different workers, and we would be wise here to take no part in this particular biogeo-graphic argument. The evidence for severe cooling at the end of the Pliocene, leading to the glacial climate, is overwhelming, but as to the necessity of the extinction of the deep sea fauna because of this change, it is not possible to take sides on the present evidence. And furthermore, having taken pains to show that adaptation to low temperature is not difficult to achieve, we must be shy about accepting the thesis that the fall in temperature as such caused widespread extinction.

To return to the general question: Elton (1930) pointed out to a somewhat unwilling audience that "adaptation is a different problem from the origin of species." Like adaptation, the origin of species depends upon the natural variability of the organism, the virtues of recombina-tion by means of sexual reproduction, and the plasticity of the genetic material, but it also depends (as adaptation does not) upon the all-impor-tant question of whether a given variant population can diverge from the parent population and find a viable place within the ecosystem. This is the process of ecosystem growth which is quite obviously as natural and universal a process as photosynthesis and respiration, and which has pro-ceeded from very small beginnings many times over in the history of life; the interest lies mainly in the limits of the process, and, in our particular reference, in how far the process of diversification can continue in the polar environments.

At the time of the beginning of life on earth; during the Devonian arrival of life on land; after the Permian ice age in the southern conti-nents; at the time of the great advances of homothermy and of flight in vertebrates; and with the drastic events of the close of the Mesozoic; at all these periods in the past new possibilities were opened up and new habitat areas and potential ecological niches became available. At such times, we should expect the rate of speciation to be high. New species do not appear "on their own," but always within an ecological framework; a living organism cannot exist either in nature or in logic except in rela-tion to its environment, both physical and biotic. It follows that the evo-lution of species implies and includes the evolution of the ecosystem; and we may speculate that the evolution of larger taxa, families, and classes implies large ecological changes in the past which make possible the suc-cess of large changes in organisms.

Several authors have speculated upon the time necessary to produce a new species, based on paleontological experience and considerations of mutation rate, and the rest. It seems to me that these figures must have little meaning, and that the rate of speciation has been highly variable in the past, being a function of ecological opportunity which must have varied greatly with circumstances and with time. The rate of speciation in, say, birds in the Cretaceous, was probably very much higher than the rate of speciation of the same group in Tertiary times, because in the Cretaceous the birds were in the process of exploiting new opportunities offered by the invasion of the air as a medium of locomotion. And in the polar regions, after the change of the Pleistocene beginnings, or the end of the Pliocene, the rate of speciation would be expected to be as rapid as the environmental conditions allowed. These environmental changes include, of course, changes in the organisms and the number of species themselves, since other organisms form part of the environment of any given species. This is what is meant by the term "bootstrap operation" used in the last chapter. Feedback, both negative and positive, is involved here, and especially positive feedback, since each addition to the complexity opens the way for still greater diversification up to the limits of the system; on reaching those limits negative feedback takes over control and the process levels off.

Let us see what sort of ecological growth has occurred, and may be expected to be occurring, in polar environments since the beginnings of the Pleistocene; and ask the question how far this process may be expected to go.

In the last ten years papers have appeared on the mechanism of the evolution of the ecological system, on the numbers of species in the world and their relative abundance, and on the contrast between the tropical and polar situations, such as those by Hutchinson (1959), MacArthur (1957, 1960), Klopfer and MacArthur (1960), Connell and Orias (1964), Dunbar (1960, 1963), Margalef (1963), Fischer (1960), and Pianka (1966). The question can perhaps best be attacked by a discussion of one of the most recent of them, that of Connell and Orias (1964), particularly because it attempts a general theory and brings together a number of points of view for evaluation. These authors, in putting forward a theory of ecological regulation and species diversity, begin by discussing five ideas which have been suggested as explaining the fact that "some areas support more kinds of organisms than others." These ideas, together with appropriate comments, are:

1. That the regions with fewer species have fewer ecological niches than those with many species. First a word on "niches": it is agreed that the niche is defined as quite different from the habitat, by "an order of difference." There are three current definitions, all of which agree in principle; that of Elton (1927), who made the point that where a species lives (habitat) is different from what it does (its "profession"); that of many contemporary ecologists, epitomised by King (1964) as "the sum of the ecological requirements of a species"; and the polydimensional "hypervolume" of Hutchinson (1957). Connell and Orias point out that the num-

ber of niches that a given area can contain is not a function of mere geography, and that it can only be described *a posteriori,* not *a priori.* This follows from the nature of the niche and from the fact that new niches develop as the ecosystem develops. It is not possible to maintain, with justice, that the Arctic tundra has fewer niches than the tropical rain forest, though we may suspect that this is so; the tundra, for all we know, might develop as many in time, although the probability is low.

2. That regions with few species, such as the Arctic, owe their poverty to the sheer rigorousness of the environment. This view has been put forward also by Wynne-Edwards (1952) in most vivid English, well worth quoting once more. In discussing the bird population of Baffin Island, and the fact that it did not appear to obey the Gausean theory of exclusion, Wynne-Edwards wrote: "Except perhaps among carnivorous predators, competition between individuals for space and nourishment seems commonly to be reduced to a low level among members of the Arctic flora and fauna; they live somewhat like weeds, the secret of whose success lies in their ability to exploit transient conditions while they last, in the absence of serious competition. In the Arctic the struggle for existence is overwhelmingly against the physical world, now sufficiently benign, now below the threshold for successful reproduction, and now so violent that life is swept away, after which recolonization alone can restore it."

The comments of Connell and Orias on this point are also highly quotable: "what could be more rigorous than the land environment for organisms evolved in water, composed chiefly of water, supported by it, and physically and chemically buffered by it? Yet the extreme success of the invasion of land is attested by the presence there of over 80 per cent of animal species (Thorson 1957). The ultimate question remains, if a few species have become adapted to any very rigorous habitat, why have not more? We conclude therefore, that rigorousness *per se* cannot be a universal explanation for lack of diversity." The only reasonable counter to this is that the invasion of the land happened a very long time ago, and that we know little about the hazards and fortunes of the pioneers; and that the time factor is almost certainly in favour of the Devonian adventurers, that is to say that the comparison of desert and polar systems of today with the Devonian pattern involves an apparent foreshortening of the Devonian time-scale which is probably very real. Anyway, the operative element here is the effect on general ecosystem growth rather than upon individual specific adaptation, so that the point made by Connell and Orias seems well taken.

3. That the difference between the tropics and the systems of higher latitudes is one of age, of maturity; the tropics have reached equilibrium and the temperate and polar regions are still immature ecologically and (pre-

sumably) still developing. This view was first put forward by none other than Wallace (1878), and has recently been revived by Wimpenny (1941), Dunbar (1960, 1963), and Fischer (1960). Connell and Orias consider that "recent evidence does not support this hypothesis," a view with which I find myself in contention. The hypothesis supposes that "the polar and temperate zones have undergone recurrent climatic catastrophes, with periodic extinctions keeping diversity low," and Newell (1962) is quoted as authority for the thesis that "fossil plants, good indicators of past climates, do not record catastrophic changes in temperature at the ends of the eras. Consequently, it appears improbable that significant temperature changes were responsible for the crises in animal life." The crises in animal life are not questioned. Newell makes the point that temperature changes would affect polar and tropical regions rather than temperate. At the poles and in the tropics, small temperature changes in climate would be expected to cause serious ecological changes (a point which does not jibe with the lack of drastic changes in vegetation), whereas the faunas of the temperate regions could simply adjust to change by shifting north or south. Whatever the truth of this, it is interesting to note that this pattern of temperature change is the same as that assumed by Matthew (1915) in his classic interpretation of "Climate and Evolution," an interpretation which still has many adherents and which may well turn out to be correct.

However that may be, there can be little wrong in interpreting the Pleistocene Ice Age as a climatic catastrophe, or at least as a drastic change which removed a great deal of life from the high latitudes, certainly on land and most probably also in the sea. And furthermore, change in temperature is not the main point, nor is extinction; the idea of ecological immaturity is based on the existence of starting points, and in particular (in Wallace's concept, for instance) on the Pleistocene change. It is not only climatic change that can cause these new beginnings; large evolutionary advances in organisms do the same thing. Whether the Pleistocene caused widespread extinction is secondary; the primary effects were the denudation of large land areas and the setting up of new environmental conditions, with temperature as one factor only, in the high latitudes; these conditions persist today.

The historical factor, therefore, cannot be dismissed out of hand, and it will be brought forward again with some force, below, in the discussion of distribution and the mechanism of ecological evolution.

4. That ecological niches are smaller in the tropics and therefore the density of species is, or can be, greater. This is based on the work of Klopfer and MacArthur (1960), and there seems to be nothing wrong with

it. Together with the suggestion of overlapping niches in the tropics, put forward by the same authors, this is in keeping with the growth of ecological systems and the maturity of tropical systems in general, and strengthens the importance of the time factor in the tropical-polar differences.

5. That there is a selective process in favour of ecological complexity and species diversity, the ultimate survival criterion being increased community stability. "Diversity would eventually be limited by unfavourable physical factors, by space, by limitations to the length of food chains, by the evolution of large body size and by the fineness of possible subdivisions of niches. In the Arctic, organic productivity may limit diversity" (Connell and Orias, *loc. cit.*). This is in fact a description of the work of Hutchinson (1959), and with reference also to the stability study of MacArthur (1955), and part of it is used by Connell and Orias in the development of their own hypothesis. It should be pointed out that here also great importance is laid on the historic aspect, on the growth of the ecosystem with time.

The hypothesis offered by Connell and Orias is interesting. Their model is shown in Fig. 14. Starting from a hypothetical increase in the physical stability of the environment, from whatever cause, the argument is that this increased stability will allow organisms to use less energy in regulatory activities required by environmental instability (in light, moisture, and especially in temperature) and thus to allocate more energy to productivity; increase in productivity in turn leads to larger populations. *Productivity* is here defined as equivalent to the net primary productivity of plants, or the secondary productivity of consumers, after Odum (1959). This is not the same definition as that used in Chapter 4 for "production," lacking as it does the factor of storage or standing crop averaged over the year; this difference in definition is immaterial for the present argument. Larger populations encourage the growth of interspecific associations and also the formation of new species, and lead thus to increased ecosystem complexity and hence to greater community stability, stability being considered as inversely proportional to population oscillations in the system. On the land, and possibly along the margins of the sea, the increased productivity in turn increases the stability of the physical environment, a phenomenon for which there is some evidence, and so the positive feedback continues.

Negative feedback, however, enters the argument at this point, in the form of smaller specific populations resulting from the increasing number of species and their growing specialization, which is interpreted as leading to decreased community stability. Other factors limiting the

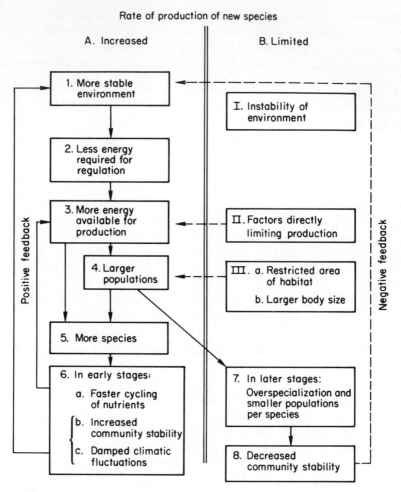

FIG. 14 Model for the production and regulation of species diversity in an ecological system, after Connell and Orias (1964). See text. Solid lines indicate an increase, dashed lines a decrease, in diversity.

growth of complexity are the direct limitation of productivity by low energy supply, as in abyssal faunas, deserts, or highly stable ocean areas (or the Arctic, one might add); lack of space for the development of large numbers of species, as on islands; large body size, which limits specific numbers; and presumably unavoidable or high-oscillation environmental instability which cannot be adequately controlled by the growth of organic complexity.

This scheme is extremely interesting, but there are certain comments which must be made upon it, in addition to those already offered above, in particular those in favour of the concept of ecological maturation with time.

1. The authors state that in building the model "it has been assumed that enough time has elapsed for ecological communities to come into a steady state in the maintenance of the particular relative abundances of species composing them"; but the model (Fig. 14) is itself the description of a process along the time dimension, and follows the ecological growth from lesser to greater stability, lesser to greater "productivity." It is difficult therefore to see what is meant by this provision, or by the rejection of the historical view and the idea of ecological evolution.

2. The authors write: "Given no difference in mutation rates, a more abundant species has more mutations because the gene pool is larger; the chance of gene fixation is also reduced in large populations. Therefore, as a consequence of greater population size, the organisms in the more stable environment possess greater intra-specific genetic variety." This is no doubt true, but the most stable environments of all are found in the tropics, where the number of species is greatest and the populations are less, per species, than in the less stable environments north and south. This statement, therefore, applies only if the reference is to the process of ecosystem development, not to the equilibrium situation which the authors insist they are describing.

3. The negative feedback applied to the growth of the ecosystem is in the form of instability following upon greater specific specialization and efficiency. This presumably is taken to occur in such systems as the tropical rain forest, but the tropical rain forest is generally taken to be the most stable of all environments, and at the same time the system showing greatest specialization and greatest refinement of adaptation, species by species, and therefore greatest efficiency.

4. "In the sea, a paradoxical situation appears to exist; although physical factors such as temperature and salinity are very stable, only about 16 per cent of animal species are found there (Thorson 1957). In addition, about three-quarters of these occur on the few hard substrates, whereas only one-fifth are in the extensive soft substances * and the remainder are in the

* At the time this book was going to press, my attention was directed to the contemporary work of Dr. Howard L. Sanders, of Woods Hole, on species diversity in marine habitats. Dr. Sanders very kindly sent me a prepublication copy of his manuscript, which describes rather high diversity in deep sea (continental slope) polychaetes and bivalves of soft bottoms. This new information should be taken into account when assessing the arguments put forward here.

plankton, which occupies most of the oceanic space." Here, it seems to me, the authors have argued themselves into a corner; having rejected the concept of the restriction of species variety by lack of habitat differentiation, they are unable to use this argument to explain this particular marine situation, and have to seek elsewhere. But surely the marine environment is obviously less rich in variety of habitat types than is the land, except in the littoral zone in low and middle latitudes. It is all very well to maintain, rightly, that ecological niches have more dimensions than do habitats, but the dimensions of habitats nevertheless form an important part of "the sum of the ecological requirements of a species," and the enormous areas and volumes of homogeneous seawater that exist cannot be left out of account.

Self-bereft of this explanation, Connell and Orias offer one which I believe few marine ecologists could accept: "The paradox vanishes when one considers the other challenges offered to aquatic organisms. The greater density of water means that turbulence of the medium imposes much greater stresses in aquatic than land organisms. In the shallow areas where the greatest productivity and fastest nutrient cycling occur the turbulence is greatest. A great proportion of the energy supply of organisms in this region is used in structures and activities which counter the challenge of massive instability of the medium." This is instability of a different colour, to begin with, and secondly the fact that productivity and species numbers are greatest precisely in this most turbulent region of the sea must mean that the turbulence is no handicap to rich ecological development. In fact the diversity and biotic stability of tropical and even temperate inshore and littoral areas probably rival those of the tropical rain forest itself, although I know of no direct studies on this question.

Having made these so many comments on this paper of Connell and Orias (1964), it is necessary to say that the paper is an important one, and that their model has much to offer towards an understanding of what actually occurs in the development of ecosystems. If it were not important it would not be worth spending so much time on it. Let us now look at the relation between energy and ecosystem evolution, and the contrasts between polar and tropical conditions from a somewhat different point of view.

Tropical, temperate, and polar systems differ in two important aspects with regard to the amounts and cycling of the energy present: (1) the total energy capital, and (2) the relation between the rate of energy turnover and energy storage. In the rain forest, and in productive (vertically unstable) marine areas in the tropics, the energy capital is large and the rate of turnover, or cycling, is high; the balance between the two is such that both the net primary production rate and the standing crop are large. That is to say, the energy available is abundant enough to maintain large standing crops in spite of the high turnover rate. Energy capital is measured in terms of (a) heat budget, (b) energy in the form of matter of all sorts—nutrients, living tissue, detritus,* and (c) kinetic energy in the form of surface winds and vertical motion in the sea. In the unproductive tropical marine areas which are highly stable in the vertical column, the available energy capital is small and the production as defined here is low, irrespective of the rate of turnover.

Temperate systems, which operate at lower temperature levels and which may involve slower growth rates than in the tropics, nevertheless show high turnover rates in spring and summer and probably considerably greater energy capital values. The storage factor is high, and the result is higher net primary production rates than in the tropics and often high crop production. This condition extends into the marine Subarctic, at least into its more southerly parts. In the Arctic Ocean, operating at still lower temperature levels and much reduced growth rates, the energy capital is small and the turnover rate is low. The capital and the growth rate are so low that only in special situations is it possible to build up significant storage of energy in the form of populations of Crustacea or of fish or trees; and in these situations, such as certain northern lakes and forests, the removal of a crop necessitates many years of growth before another crop is available.

The Antarctic waters are in a category by themselves in this classification, for although they operate on a low heat budget and low turnover rate, their energy capital as a whole is very high, owing to abundant upwelling and consequent rapid accumulation of matter in the biological cycle. In spite of low heat supply the total capital is so large that the crop production is very high.

Over long periods of time the heat budgets of the three major zones may be taken as constant, so that ecological development must consist of the gradual accumulation of capital in the form of nutrients, living substance, and detritus; and at some time in the past every ecological system on earth must have started with none of these things, the polar systems being the youngest of all.

It would be unwise to assume that the rate of energy turnover, which involves the growth rates and lifetimes of organisms, is a direct effect of the temperature levels of the system. Quite apart from the part played in the control of growth rate by the amount of food available, which is obvi-

* See footnote, page 37.

ously important and often decisive, we have seen that growth rate can be regulated with respect to temperature if the ultimate advantages favour such regulation. There is no reason to believe that the rate of energy turnover and the storage factor in the cycle are not evolved by means of selection as are other biological characteristics, morphological and physiological, and it is in fact not difficult to see how this might come about and what the operating influences and survival values might be. In polar regions, two ultimate objectives for selection present themselves at once —ecological adaptation to an environment which is unstable in certain parameters in which seasonal variations are large, and the trend toward greater biotic stability. The effects of both these selective forces can be discerned in the present polar ecological systems.

In both Antarctic and Arctic, but particularly in the Arctic, as has already been described in Chapter 4, there is a wide difference between winter and summer conditions, not in temperature, in which the annual range is fairly small, but in the supply of plant nutrients and in the abundance of the plants themselves. In other words, there is a large seasonal oscillation in the means of livelihood, or food, for both plants and animals. This oscillation is caused (at the proximate level) in part by low temperature, which slows down the rate of mineralization of detritus by bacteria, in part (in the sea) by the vertical stability of the water column which is often established very early in the summer and may remain throughout the year, and in part by the lack of light in the winter. These conditions exist also in temperate regions, but in much lesser amplitude, and are probably insignificant in the tropics except for the high stability of the upper water in the nonproductive marine areas. To this highly oscillating availability of food the living communities of both land and sea must adapt as best they can, and they will do so, we must suppose, if we hold to the orthodox neo-Darwinian system, in terms of survival value to the individual and hence to the species (see also Chapter 8, below).

At the same time, the ecological systems of polar regions will grow, if possible, in the direction of greater stability of the community, or ecosystem stability, in the same way as communities elsewhere, along the lines put forward by Hutchinson (1957, 1959), MacArthur (1955), Dunbar (1960), and Connell and Orias (1964), just discussed. Ecosystem stability is the continued existence of the system without significant oscillation in the total mass of living material or in the population numbers of the species which form the communities contained in the system. Such an idealized condition no doubt exists nowhere, but the approach to it has advantages in terms of both specific and ecosystem survival, as has been shown by many workers and most recently by MacArthur (1955). It is achieved by developing maximum complexity (diversity of species) and maximum rate of flow of energy through the system. It is realized to the greatest degree in tropical environments, less in temperate zones, and least in polar regions. It does not necessarily lead to greatest crop production in the sense used here; this will depend upon the level of the energy capital.

The end results of these two processes of selection are not necessarily the same and may in fact conflict—this greatly adds to the interest of the study and demands a balance between the two processes which must be set up to the net advantage of the community. The high amplitude of seasonal oscillation would be expected to select for slow growth (except in special circumstances), low metabolism, large body size, high specific fecundity, increased energy capital, low energy turnover, high energy storage, and small number of species. Selection towards greater ecosystem stability should select for larger number of species, lower specific fecundity, higher energy turnover, higher energy capital, and probably smaller body size and lower energy storage. Adaptation to the oscillation of environment and the advantages of ecosystem stability are thus to a large degree in competition in ecosystem development. This requires considerable elaboration, which is provided in the next chapter.

Chapter 6

ECOLOGICAL ADAPTATION AND
EVOLUTION (II)

Adaptation to Environmental Oscillation

McLaren (1964) has pointed out that perhaps the most demanding stress to which Arctic organisms are exposed is that of the short productive season and the long winter, when food is in short supply. In response to this they may do one or more of a variety of things: adjust their life cycle to the unit time of one year between productive seasons, either by one-, two-, or more year cycles, according to body size; grow to a large body size to give either a large number of small eggs or an adequate number of large eggs per female; store up enough energy in the productive season to last the individual until the next; live at a low metabolic level (consistent with minimum locomotory requirements) during most of the year, as in the dormant stages of land poikilotherms.

These adjustments are interconnected. Thus large body size is correlated with high egg number in the plankton, usually in a nonlinear manner (McLaren 1963), and often with large egg size in the benthos (Thorson 1950). Large body size and low metabolism are also related, as are large size and energy storage; and the adjustment of the life cycle to the twelve-month unit, which tends to eliminate reproduction at times other than the short summer period of food production, is obviously related to slow growth in small animals. Slow growth may be forced upon Arctic organisms by scarcity of food as a proximate adjustment, but the onset of maturity is clearly imposed at the ultimate level by the annual oscillation; it was pointed out in Chapter 2 that the two-phase or polyphase breeding cycle seen in Arctic plankton and in insects appears to be an "all or nothing" arrangement, at least in species above a certain low limit of body size, so that if the normal life cycle takes two years in a given region, a one-year cycle in the same species is not found there, nor is there a tendency to breed more than once a year. Exceptions to this may exist, but not in the Arctic proper, where the productive season is shortest. This special matter of breeding cycles is concerned with general considerations of body size and growth rate, and has recently been reexamined.

In small species with life cycles of one year or less, overlapping generations are not the rule. Such organisms normally have seasonally controlled development, so that the progress of the seasons keeps the generations in step. In the plankton, for example, the first generation of the spring may produce succeeding generations during the summer, one after the other, until the overwintering generation appears in the autumn. In cooler temperate regions there may be only one generation per year, as is found typically in the euphausids and chaetognaths. Copepods, being smaller, usually continue to produce more than one brood per year even in the fringes of the Subarctic. In west Greenland and in Ungava Bay, however, *Calanus* and *Pseudocalanus* breed only once a year (Fontaine 1955, Maclcllan 1967) and there is recent evidence that in the Arctic water further north *Pseudocalanus* takes two years to reach maturity and *Calanus* even longer (Cairns 1965).

Overlapping generations thus are common in small invertebrates, both aquatic and terrestrial, in the higher latitudes. If each mature individual breeds only once, the two broods which coexist in any given area are reproductively isolated from each other, unless the system goes out of phase for some reason. Since breeding periods tend to be short and seasonal in polar plankton, as in insects, the two-phase cycle normally involves a two-year life cycle. It was originally thought that this was necessitated simply by the slow growth caused by low temperature, in animals of relevant size; but McLaren (1966) has recently suggested that in fact the two-year cycle may have evolved (rather than a one-year or three-year lifetime) because the relation between body size and egg number confers a very definite advantage of greater fecundity upon the two-year life, taking the normal mortality rate into consideration, and that the one-year life in the Arctic and Subarctic would be automatically eliminated.

McLaren's study is based on the chaetognath *Sagitta elegans,* whose breeding cycle is well documented throughout its wide range from temperate to Arctic waters; it produces five or six generations in the year in the English Channel, probably only one per year in the Gulf of St. Lawrence, with a one-year life span, and has a two-phase cycle with two-year life span in west Greenland and the Canadian Eastern Arctic. By shifting its growth-temperature response a little further than it does, in northern waters, it could breed at the end of one year instead of two, or so at least it is assumed; but McLaren calculates that if it did so the realized rate of increase would be negative and that the annual decrease of the population would be about thirty-five per cent. This conclusion is reached by relating, from direct observation, egg number to body size in the northern populations, and taking the egg number corresponding to the mean size of the one-year-olds as the egg number which would be produced per female if in fact the population matured at one year. This assumption is open to question, for if the onset of maturation is to be put forward to one year instead of two, then presumably it would be a comparatively simple matter also to adjust the relation between ovary development and temperature, to give a larger egg number. Nevertheless the conclusions may be sound, even if difficult to prove, and it may well be that the large size attained by *Sagitta* and other forms showing the two-year cycle is attributable to this fecundity effect.

It might be inserted here that it is no longer possible to maintain that the very slow growth of plankton copepods in Arctic water, to take one example, is indicative of poor adaptation to the environment, as was suggested by Digby (1954) (see page 21 above). Whatever the particular relevance of the two-year cycle may be, there is little doubt that in most cases slow growth is associated with large size and hence high fecundity, and it also adjusts to the long period between the production times of the phytoplankton.

The question of metabolic rate has been dealt with in Chapter 2, but the present state of our knowledge is clearly not satisfactory. Metabolic regulation with respect to temperature in aquatic organisms has been measured in the summer only, when food supply is adequate; we still know nothing about the winter metabolism of the Arctic plankton or benthos. On land, metabolism in winter falls to very low levels in poikilotherms in which dormancy is the rule; this follows from the extremes of low temperature to which they are exposed. Low energy turnover of the whole system follows from large individual body size, from the low growth rates, and from the stored energy in individuals; low winter metabolism in aquatic animals is certainly to be expected, but whether it falls below the resting levels measured in summer is not known.

Examples of these evolutionary developments can be found everywhere in the Arctic flora and fauna. Large size in Arctic planktonic forms and in terrestrial poikilotherms has been known for many years, and has been attributed to various influences, such as the lack of the necessity for greater flotation powers in the more viscous water when compared with warm water faunas, the possible delay in sexual maturity owing to low energy of the environment, and even to a Bergmann effect. It is probable that these are not seriously to be considered, and that the causes of the phenomenon, at the ultimate level, are the advantage of greater fecundity and possibly the greater efficiency of the use of food resources (see p. 77).

Selection toward adjustment to seasonal oscillation should lead also to a small number of species, in that unless specific populations are large there would be serious danger, due to winter mortality, of reducing the population to levels from which reproductive recovery would be unlikely or impossible; and since the total energy capital is small it follows that, if populations are to be reasonably large, the number of species must be small. The number is indeed small in polar communities, and there are few if any that can be called "rare" in the naturalist's sense. Moreover from what we have learned about the apparent ease with which animals can adapt, individually and therefore specifically, to the "hardships of the Arctic," these rigors themselves can scarcely be blamed for the poverty of the Arctic fauna. It must be attributed to one or more of three factors: the high environmental oscillation, the low energy capital, and the immaturity of the system.

The small species numbers are well-known in general, but it may be interesting to bring together some estimates of species numbers which compare the Arctic with other regions or with world totals for several taxonomic groups: of the approximately 8600 species of birds in the world, about 70 breed in the Arctic, land and sea, as defined here, and most of them are migrants. There are some 3200 species of mammals in the world, of which only 23 are known on the land north of the tree line; for the total number of Arctic mammals, some five or six sea mammals should be added, giving a total of less than 30. Reptiles and Amphibia are not cold-adapted at all; there are no Arctic reptiles and only one amphibian, the wood frog, can be said to penetrate the Arctic, and not very impressively at that. The fishes are extremely poorly represented in the Arctic. The world is full of fish, the total number of species being variously estimated between 23,000 and 30,000, but the number found in Arctic water is quite small, probably less than 50. Arctic species in the shelf fauna of North America number about 30, and Ekman (1953) gives as "roughly 15" the number of deep-water species below 600 metres. Figures are not available for most of the invertebrate groups. Downes (1964) estimates that of the vast numbers of insect species known, perhaps 300, exclusive of the Collembola, are found in the Canadian Arctic Islands. Two crustacean taxa, of less than ordinal rank, have been studied enough to be quotable here, namely the gammarid Amphipoda and the calanoid Copepoda. The world list of gammarids (Barnard 1958) has approximately 4200 species in it, of which the number of truly Arctic forms is probably about 200 [Gurjanova (1951) lists 451 species as "Arctic," but she includes in this term such decidedly Subarctic areas as the Barents Sea]. There are only some 20 calanoid copepods which can be called truly Arctic; perhaps this number is too large. The world list of this group has not been published; Sars (1903) described 106 species from Norwegian waters, and the total number of species recognized is about 400.

Selection Toward Ecosystem Stability

The idea that the ecosystems of the higher latitudes are less mature than those of the tropics was first suggested by Alfred Russel Wallace (1878), and it has been developed recently by several authors (Margalef 1963, Dunbar 1960, 1963, and Fischer 1960). Wallace emphasized that the faunas and floras of temperate and polar zones had been subjected to periodic climatic catastrophes, in the manner of the older theory of Cuvier, causing widespread extinction. Whereas periods of considerable and abnormal extinction appear to have occurred, the matter is still controversial, and in any event they are not necessary to the theory of ecosystem maturation. As has been pointed out in the last chapter, large changes, either in environments or in organisms, set ecological growth going along new paths, all of which will be expected to involve growth toward maturity. The Pliocene-Pleistocene climatic change is such an event, and the possibility that polar ecosystems are young and still unstable, and in process of development toward more stable maturity, must therefore be taken seriously.

It is generally considered that the process of evolution is one of the development from simple to more complex patterns, a belief which should not be allowed to go completely unchallenged. It is no doubt true that the vertebrate eye is far more complex anatomically than the ocellus of the coelenterate, and that the copepod gives the impression of greater structural complexity than does the earthworm. Such apparent greater complexity, however, may be superficial only, and it seems moreover that while a "more advanced" group may be more elaborate in one respect than its ancestors, it may be less elaborate in another. Certainly there is progression toward greater simplicity, the reverse of complexity, in the evolutionary changes between the skull of the Paleozoic fish and that of the Tertiary mammal. The same is true of the limbs in most vertebrate lines, and there can be no doubt whatever that the single cell, and its analogues the protozoan and the bacterium, are now displaying a structural complexity so impressive that we can no longer assume that the first stirrings of life on earth spent much time as simple blobs of protoplasm. This aspect of increasing simplicity, rather than the reverse, in evolution, is probably what D'Arcy Thompson had in mind when he wrote:

"Organic evolution has its physical analogue in the universal law that the world tends, in all its parts and particles, to pass from certain less probable to certain more probable configurations or states. This is the second law of thermodynamics. It has been called *the law of the evolution of the world;* and we call it, after Clausius, the Principle of *En-*

tropy, which is a literal translation of *Evolution* into Greek." * (D'Arcy Thompson 1948, p. 11.)

Although the general rule of evolution toward complexity may have to be qualified somewhat with respect to anatomical evolution, it seems to hold well in ecological evolution, in which it may reasonably be postulated that the simple ecosystems, being subject to violent oscillation in numbers of individual species, have this built-in flaw of the danger of self-extinction, and that there will be a selection toward greater stability, in the sense already defined, and hence toward enhanced viability. It has long been a tenet of ecological theory that stability is given to ecosystems by the development of more complex food chains, or food webs, and thus by increase in the numbers of species in the system, as has already been discussed by Hutchinson (1959) and demonstrated by MacArthur (1955).

Evolution toward greater stability, therefore, in favouring increasing numbers of species † must, in Arctic situations, work contrary to ecological adaptation to the highly oscillating environment, which tends to keep the number of species small. There are other elements in which the two processes come into conflict. Selection toward stability will favour lower specific fecundity, because lower fecundity will reduce the rate of specific population growth and thus reduce the amplitude of population oscillation. It will also favour high energy turnover and lesser energy storage, and thus tend also toward smaller rather than larger body size.

Both processes would favour increased energy capital, that is to say the gradual growth of the total mass of living and nonliving elements in the biotic cycle. The two evolutionary processes, mainly in conflict but partly not, are summarized in Table 2. It remains now to see to what extent the two processes have achieved their ends in polar regions.

A comparison of the effects shown in Table 2 with the phenomena found in nature leaves no doubt about which side is winning at present. Arctic populations, as already demonstrated, exhibit high fecundity, large body size, slow growth, and small numbers of species; the resulting ecosystems are simple and unstable. The high environmental oscillation, which is overwhelmingly the result of the Pleistocene event, has put its stamp upon the biosphere of the polar regions. Also, with special reference to the Antarctic and to the Subarctic (but not the Arctic), the physical factors of atmosphere and hydrosphere have allowed for the accumulation of large available energy capital. This is favoured by both selection systems, as is also the development of large eggs in certain circumstances.

---

* Entropy is in fact not the translation of "evolution" into Greek. It is curious that such an eminent classicist should have said so, but the derivation of "entropy" is not the point here. The point is the interesting interpretation of organic evolution.

† See also p. 79.

The next question is whether this situation is an established end result, implying that it is settled and "permanent," or whether the evolution of the polar ecosystems is still in its comparative infancy, so that we might expect changes in the direction of the right-hand column in Table 2. To this the first answer must be that nothing in nature is ever static, but that change is always the rule—"Change itself is the only reality" (Hippocrates); and second, it is not reasonable to believe that the natural development toward ecological stability, which is seen in other ecosystems, will not also be pressed in polar zones. The belief that there must always

TABLE 2 Effects of selection toward two different evolutionary objectives, described in text.

Toward adaptation to environmental oscillation, selection favours:	Toward ecosystem stability (maturity), selection favours:
1. High fecundity given by	1. Low specific fecundity, given partly by
2. Large body size with many eggs. This is given by	2. Small body size with few small eggs, or large size with few large eggs
3. Slow growth to maturity (slow energy turnover);	3. Fast growth to maturity (small eggs), or slow growth (large eggs)
4. Small number of species, giving	4. Large number of species, giving
5. Simple ecosystem	5. Complex ecosystem

Both objectives are favoured by:
6. Increased energy capital

be pressure toward stability has been expressed by many authors, with good evidence, and the present writer has already put forward instances of apparent attempts, as it were, to achieve greater stability in the Arctic (Dunbar 1960).

The proper course of reasoning, therefore, is to accept the present condition as the consequence of selection toward immediate adjustment to serious oscillation in environmental conditions and to consider what signs there are of evolution toward something a little better.

The simple ecosystem, in which the number of species is small and the fecundity of individual species usually very high, is subject to population oscillations whose periods are functions of the size of the animals. In the size range of copepods, the oscillation in polar regions is annual; in lemmings the period is from three to five years, in the American Partridge ten years. In all cases the slump in numbers at troughs of low population carries with it the danger of local extinction of the oscillator, and since the oscillations are greatest in the herbivores, such extinctions are dangerous to higher trophic levels and could thus, on this view, cause the local extinction of the whole ecosystem owing to the lack of alternative species at the several trophic levels. Evolution toward greater stability involves changes in the system which would tend to increase the number of species, lower specific fecundity, and spread the consumption of the food supply over as large a portion of the 12-month period as possible. These objectives are accomplished by subdividing habitats and niches to allow the introduction of new species into the system, by producing only a small number of eggs or offspring (which is compatible with either large or small body size depending upon the type of egg), and by using the total basic food supply adequately, which means using detritus and dissolved organic material as well as living plants. These processes are interrelated, and there is evidence that they have been evolved in certain instances, and are elsewhere in process of evolution. The evidence can briefly be presented under the following headings:

1. *Continued plant growth in winter.* Rodhe (1955), working on northern Swedish lakes, found that the zooplankton continued to grow during the winter, although net samples and counts with the Utermöhl sedimentation technique showed no plankton algae which could serve as food for the zooplankton. Other techniques, however, showed that "even the most extreme oligotrophic lakes . . . have indeed a winter phytoplankton consisting of very small green-algae (size $1-2\mu$ or less) and somewhat larger but partly very fragile flagellates." Rodhe concluded that these algal populations, normally autotrophic, were facultative heterotrophs and could feed on dissolved organic matter when the light intensity was too low for photosynthesis. To quote again from his paper: "the algae growing during winter darkness can hardly be primary producers but assimilate dissolved organic substances resulting from photosynthesis during the previous light period. The subarctic lake can be said to act as an electrical battery: it utilizes and gives out energy with which it has been charged earlier." There are also experimental results (Provasoli and Pintner 1953) showing that several planktonic algal species, maintained in culture in the laboratory, may be both autotrophic and heterotrophic.

This work has not yet been followed up in saltwater environments, but it opens the possibility of continued basic organic production in polar conditions generally, throughout the year, which would temper the otherwise extreme oscillation of the polar and subpolar food supply. It also underlines another possibility which needs investigating, namely that the zooplankton may make good use of dissolved organic substances as direct food supply in winter, which in turn would explain how it is possible for certain Arctic invertebrates to produce their young during the winter, as is described below.

2. *Photosynthesis on the under surface of sea ice.* Organic synthesis is extended in both space and time by the ability of algal cells to photosynthesize under sea ice in very low light intensities; this has been demonstrated in the Arctic by Apollonio (1961), and in the Antarctic by Bunt (1964), and has been mentioned in Chapter 4 above. This appears to involve the evolution of a specialized flora, for the photosynthesis is apparently inhibited by an increase in light intensity above the very low levels existing beneath snow-covered ice several feet in thickness. This special food supply is used by the "ice-grazers," such as the amphipod *Gammarus wilkitzki,* and provides food some time before the normal phytoplanktonic supply develops when the ice melts. Again, this tends somewhat to reduce the suddenness and severity of the Arctic environmental oscillation.

3. *Winter spawning.* Many species in the Arctic and Subarctic are now known to produce their young during the winter, when the food supply is presumably minimal. In a situation in which the spring bloom of phytoplankton is sudden and violent, one would have expected that all animal species which depended on phytoplankton as food for the young would have evolved a breeding cycle that would release the young at some time between the beginning and the peak of the phytoplankton production. Many, perhaps most, species of course do this, notably the copepods, but there are many that do not, and as the study of Arctic breeding cycles continues, more such species appear. MacGinitie (1955) gives many examples of invertebrate species in the waters of the Point Barrow region, Alaska, which begin to develop their eggs in October and later, and many which produce ripe eggs at that time; some of the amphipods had hatched young in the brood pouch. Dunbar (1957) recorded the abundant Arctic pelagic amphipod *Parathemisto libellula* as maturing late in the autumn or early winter and carrying hatched young in December. *Gammarus setosus* breeds in the colder part of the year, differing in this respect from its close relative *G. oceanicus* (MacIntyre 1959); and among the 114 species of amphipods taken in Ungava Bay (Dunbar 1954), consisting of large material collected over four seasons, only 55 species were found to include ovigerous or paedigerous females in the spring and summer months, from June to September. The material collected by the Russian drifting station in the Arctic Ocean in 1950–51 included several species recorded as spawning in winter (Brodskii and Nikitin 1955).

This winter breeding has the effect of increasing the number of species in the system; it is analogous to the adoption of nocturnal or diurnal habit within a given area, and it also spreads the rate of predation on the available food supply more evenly over the year. The findings of Rodhe, quoted above, are clearly highly relevant to this phenomenon.

4. *Size and growth rate.* Earlier in this chapter (Table 2) it was pointed out that slow growth to large size was a development to be expected in ecological adaptation to a highly oscillating environment; it probably also has advantages in adaptation toward greater ecosystem stability in that it would tend to raise the total biomass present at any given time, and hence this slow growth appears also in the right-hand column in Table 2. Harvey (1957), in a discussion of growth and metabolism in marine poikilotherms, writes: "In addition to this general inverse relation between age or size of animals and losses by respiration, there is an inverse relation between age and growth rate (the daily percentage increase in organic matter). It appears usual that growth rate decreases more rapidly with increasing size than respiration decreases . . . . In consequence, a greater proportion of food assimilated by young animals is built into new tissue than by old animals. Hence the same rate of plant production may permit a greater biomass of a stable community consisting mostly of aged, larger, slow-growing, slow-respiring animals than of one mainly composed of small quick-growing animals. The latter fauna, however, may synthesize more animal tissue yearly, the rate of turnover of living tissue in the animals being greater." Harvey's presentation of this is shown in Fig. 15.

It may seem paradoxical at first sight to demand both slow growth and fast growth, small size and large size, as adaptations toward the same evolutionary end; but we are dealing here with the evolution of the ecological system as a whole, and the system includes a greater or larger number of species which are not bound to develop all in the same direction. Diversification of evolutionary patterns at the specific level is in fact to be expected. Toward the goal of ecosystem stability, fast growth and small size favour greater turnover and (in a reasonably complex system) lesser specific oscillation; slow growth and large size give greater efficiency of the use of the available resources. It is not theoretically impossible that large and small body size might develop within the same species.

5. *Planktonic larvae of benthonic animals.* The work of Thorson (1950, 1952) on planktonic larvae of shallow water benthos has already been mentioned in Chapter 2 in connection with growth rate regulation; it is relevant also to the present issue. Thorson found that in temperate and Arctic regions the pelagic larva may or may not be retained in the life cycle. If it is retained, the spawning is restricted to a short period in the spring, coinciding with the abundance of the spring plankton; if it is not, the spawning period is much longer and could extend throughout

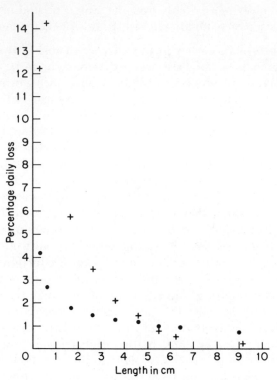

FIG. 15 Relation between daily loss of organic matter due to respiration (black circles), daily increase in organic matter due to growth (crosses) and length in *Mytilus edulis*. Redrawn from Harvey (1957), after Jorgensen.

the year. There is a direct relationship, whether causal or not, between the mean temperature of the environment and the proportion of species which retain the pelagic larva, so that in polar regions a very high proportion have abandoned the attempt to adjust to the environmental oscillation and have retreated, as it were, to the full-time use of detrital and bacterial food on the sea floor. The stabilizing effect of the loss of larva and the production of larger eggs is thus best developed in the high latitudes.

Related to this effect also is the observation recorded by Steele (1959), working on the shallow-water Amphipoda of the eastern Canadian Arctic. Steele found that whereas the littoral (intertidal) species have developed short breeding periods in the spring or summer, the benthonic forms as a rule breed all the year round.

6. *Two-phase breeding cycles.* The type of breeding cycle described above (this chapter), in which two broods (or more, in polyphase cycles) exist together in the same area or body of water, and in which each individual breeds only once per lifetime, gives a situation in which the two broods are reproductively isolated, the one from the other, and gene-flow between the two can occur only if the system goes out of phase so that a proportion of individuals breeds after one or three years of life, instead of two. Such a situation must be supposed to encourage divergence and ultimately speciation, and thus lead to an increase in the number of species in the ecosystem. It is not impossible that some of the systematic variants described below have arisen by this mechanism.

7. *Intraspecific variants.* Recent systematic and biogeographical work on the marine fauna suggests that intraspecific variants, or "morphs," both morphological and physiological, are significantly more common in cool temperate, Subarctic, and Arctic environments than they are in the tropics and subtropics; the same may possibly be also true for terrestrial habitats. If this is so, it points to contemporary evolution of new species, and hence to the increase in the total species numbers. Since this is a new and rather large subject, it is dealt with separately in the next chapter.

In closing this chapter, it should be pointed out that although greater ecological stability has been seen here as being favoured by, among other things, complexity manifested in larger numbers of species, it is also reasonable to suppose, as has been suggested, that the effects of larger numbers of species with narrow ecological demands could also be achieved by a smaller number of species whose demands or capabilities were wide— for instance by omnivorous habit. In theory this is acceptable, and it may be that this path toward stability is in fact shown in nature, but much more detailed study of specific habits and versatility is required before this point can be validly made.

Chapter 7

BIOGEOGRAPHY, SYSTEMATICS, AND
ECOSYSTEM DEVELOPMENT

The close relation between biogeography and systematics is now a biological commonplace; in fact it has a respectable history going back to the time of Alfred Russel Wallace. The study of biogeography in general is in a phase of heightened activity at present, largely following upon the recognition of the fact that extended geographic distribution, and geographic isolation, form the most common basic condition for the evolution of new species. Developments in ecological theory, in particular the study of niche diversification and the concept of the maturation of the ecosystem, have given new meaning to the simple operation of plotting and comparing specific distributions; so has the recent and present study of climatic change, which is reflected in change in the geography of plants and animals. With respect specifically to marine distributions, the growth and refinement of the plankton indicator technique, the emphasis on water masses rather than on the classical "biogeographic provinces," and new work on the temperature relations of growth and breeding cycles, have provided added stimulus.

In this chapter it is proposed that change in ecosystems, in the natural course of events and especially toward greater ecosystem complexity, is manifested in, and heralded by, apparent anomalies of distribution and the presence of established morphological varieties, or "morphs"; and that the profusion of such morphs of various kinds in the higher latitudes is an indication of constant evolutionary change and growth in the present geological period. The thesis applies to ecological systems in general, but marine examples are used here. The argument is as follows:

1. Distribution range is a function of environmental factors and the responses, tolerances, etc., of organisms with respect to those factors. Tem-

perature is generally considered to be of first importance here, but at the proximate level only.

2. Specific populations vary within themselves in relation to the different parts of distribution ranges. Therefore there is no reason to expect that the environment of population A in area A_1 should be the same in all respects as that of population B in area B_1 of the same "species." That is, one would expect tolerances, within a species, not to be the same over the whole geographic range.

3. This variability explains the apparent anomalies of distribution which we find, "anomalies" being interpreted in terms of the persisting (Linnaean) belief that species do *not* vary. A new taxonomic system is needed, something newer than the New Systematics.

4. The ecosystem is dynamic, and demonstrates and reflects the process and stage of evolution at any given time.

5. In the same general category as differences in physiological tolerances come morphological variants, here called *morphs,* and also species complexes and groups which have shown themselves to be difficult to resolve taxonomically. Such morphs appear to be remarkably abundant in temperate and subpolar regions.

6. The fixation of variability, that is, what variables are selected into the population, is controlled by the ecological possibilities, and in a simple situation the tendency is toward greater complexity, so that the apparent anomalies of distribution are to be considered as exmples of ecosystem growth in that direction.

7. In the polar regions, although the ecosystems may appear to be in temporary equilibrium on the shorter time-scale, and although their simplicity may be explicable in terms of low productivity and seasonal oscillation, there is a constant development in complexity.

The study bears upon the commonly expressed complaint of physical oceanographers who work together with fisheries biologists, namely that "once you have described the environment, what more can be done?" The next step is to discover where and in what way the environmental requirements or tolerances of a given species vary from the norm or from those of other parts of the specific population, and to make sure whether or not the environmental parameters studied are all that are in fact effective. And before this can be done, the precise distribution range must be known and compared with the parameters used.

Distributions

The term *distribution* is used here not in the sense of pattern of disper-
sion, as discussed by Hutchinson (1953) and others, but in the sense of
the total geographic range of a species, in the biogeographic context. In
marine biogeography the modern base-line is Ekman's 1935 classic, which
appeared revised in English translation as recently as 1953. It is witness to
the rapid growth of this field that the revision had to be considerable, and
in the past decade our knowledge of marine biogeography has grown
faster still. For present purposes I have selected certain examples of distribution which raise questions of intraspecific variation and ecosystem
change.

The euphausid *Meganyctiphanes norvegica* belongs essentially to Atlantic water, and is known as far south as the Mediterranean. In the waters
west of Greenland it is known northward to Disko Bay and westward to
the western end of Hudson Strait, but is absent in Hudson Bay (Dunbar
1964). It has not so far been taken in Baffin Bay; in the Barents Sea it is
described by Drobysheva (1957) as being brought to that area by warm
Atlantic water and as being dependent for its abundance from year to
year upon the fluctuations in the annual hydrographic regime. There are
several records, however, from shallow water in the fjords and coastal
regions of northeast Greenland (Stephensen 1933a, 1943; Sivertsen 1935),
in which Atlantic water has never been found, and to which the penetration of Atlantic water is improbable, since it would require an upwelling
from depths of 300 metres or more, for which there is no evidence nor any
presently conceivable mechanism.

The same apparently anomalous presence in northeast Greenland is
also found in *Thysanoessa longicaudata,* of which there are records also
in Scoresby Sound; this species is known from northeast Baffin Bay, but
only in regions known to be influenced by Atlantic water (Dunbar 1964).
The littoral and shallow water amphipod *Gammarus oceanicus* shows
much the same pattern (Steele 1964 and Dunbar 1954).

The Hyperiid amphipod *Parathemisto gaudichaudi* is a Subarctic
species which reaches also somewhat to the south of the Subarctic mixed-
water zone. It is not known from East Greenland coastal water and it
appears to be absent from most of Baffin Bay; but there is one record
from Smith Sound (Stephensen 1933b) and one from northwestern Foxe
Basin, both of which, and especially the latter, are outside the known
influence of Atlantic water.

Other such examples could be cited, such as the presence of *Thysanoessa raschii* and *T. inermis* in Nares Strait, between Ellesmere Island

and northwest Greenland (Shen 1966). They can be interpreted in one of three different ways, all of them arguments from ignorance: (1) the anomalous distribution records are freaks, resulting from hazards of wind or currents, and do not represent a normal situation; (2) they are due to water movements which may be normal but which have not yet been demonstrated; (3) they are due to the existence of physiological races with tolerances different from, or beyond, the normal known specific range. The first explanation is difficult to accept in most cases, for instance in the northeast Greenland anomalies cited here. The records come from several expeditions in different years, and in general the cry of "freak" may be considered the refuge of the lazy. The second is possible but quite improbable, considering the advances in oceanographic research and methods. This leaves the third, which is the answer recommended here and which, as shown below, can be allied to other sources of evidence for the existence of a great deal of intraspecific variation, physiological, ecological and morphological, in the sea and on land.

Also under the heading of distribution problems, but without apparent local anomalies, come the many species in the sea which have surprisingly wide north-south ranges, the so-called "boreo-arctic" species found normally in temperate water, Subarctic mixed water, and pure Arctic water. These are found both in the plankton and in the benthos. Out of 114 species of amphipod Crustacea taken in Ungava Bay, for example (Dunbar 1954), no less than 27 fall into this category, with the possibility of several others as well. Many other examples are found in other groups, especially in the Mollusca and the Annelida. From a considerable amount of experimental work (summarized in Chapter 2) we know that there is often a wide geographic difference in metabolic ability, or metabolic adjustment, in those species of this type which have been studied, and they may therefore be regarded as groups of metabolic races, or as species with wide metabolic clinal variation.

Taxonomic Difficulties, "Phases," and "Morphs"

The tropical variety of species, in all groups, presents a pattern at first bewildering in the numbers of its units, but a second look soon shows us that although the numbers are great, the species are sensibly distinct and behave themselves taxonomically. That is to say, they do not, in general, give trouble to the systematist or raise great problems of taxonomic decision. The variety both of habitat types and of ecological niches has sorted out the primeval variable material into discrete species, each as a rule with a relatively small habitat and degree of ecological freedom. This is not true of temperate faunas and floras, and it seems that the higher the geographic latitude the worse the taxonomic problems become, at least to the Subarctic.

This is both to be expected and to be exploited. In the higher latitudes, as in the depths of the ocean, environmental conditions can be, and usually are, the same or very similar over enormous areas, in contrast to the tropical rain forest or the complicated pattern of inshore and littoral warm-water regions. This produces much intraspecific variation, the beginnings of speciation, so that the large areas of similar type with their relatively small number of species contain within their nature the seeds of ecological diversification and their own subdivision.

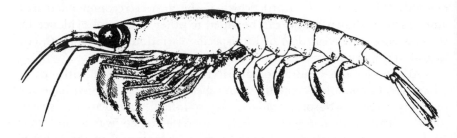

FIG. 16   *Thysanoessa inermis;* the typical form. From Einarsson (1945).

There are very many examples of these difficult groups. The order Amphipoda is full of them, such as the families Pleustidae, Stenothoidae, Lysianassidae, and Gammaridae. The family Oedicerotidae contains the genus *Westwoodilla,* a typical case of taxonomic confusion over the North Atlantic Subarctic region, to which I have drawn attention before (Dunbar 1954). The genus *Gammarus* has achieved an almost enviable notoriety among carcinologists. There are examples also in the Isopoda; *Mesidothea sabini* is considerably different morphologically in its Beaufort Sea and Hudson Bay populations, and also in its reproductive mechanism —the Hudson Bay form producing much fewer and much larger eggs (Bray 1962)—so that problems of appropriate nomenclature arise. In the Copepoda, *Calanus finmarchicus* (in the old sense), perhaps the most studied crustacean of them all, turns out after decades of close examination to consist of a whole complex of species differing in size, distribution, and in slight but definite morphological characters (Yaschnov 1955, 1961). The genus *Pseudocalanus* may be in similar need of revision.

These are examples of problems which systematists either accept as unsolved as yet or as approaching resolution in the ordinary course of their work. There are other cases which have simply been shelved by the use of the word "variety," a word which today must mean either everything or nothing in this context, but which is seldom used within the modern theoretical framework. The North Atlantic members of the euphausid genus *Thysanoessa* are three, *longicaudata, inermis,* and *raschii. T. longicaudata* has an elongated second pair of thoracic legs and eyes divided into two parts by a constriction. *T. raschii and T. inermis* do not normally show these characters in the adult, the legs being of normal length and the eyes undivided (Figs. 16, 17); but in *inermis,* according to Hansen (1911) and Einarsson (1945) and others, the younger subadult stages frequently are of *longicaudata* type both in the legs and the eyes, and not infrequently these characters persist into the mature stage. This variety

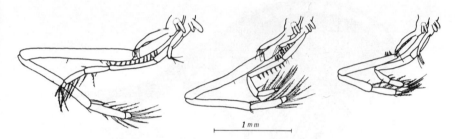

1 mm

FIG. 17 Variation in the length and thickness of the second thoracic leg of *Thysanoessa inermis* in late larval stage furcilia VII. From Einarsson (1945).

is known as *"neglecta"* and was at one time given full specific rank as *T. neglecta.*

The hyperiid amphipod *Parathemisto gaudichaudi* manifests itself in at least two forms, formerly given specific status as *Euthemisto compressa* and *E. bispinosa* (Figs. 18, 19); there also appears to be an intermediate type. They differ in the shape and setation of the third and fifth peraeopods and in the development of dorsal spines. Stephensen (1923) showed that the two forms cannot always be separated, particularly in the southern parts of the range, as individuals may combine characters of both, and Barnard (1932) brought the two forms together and showed that they were the same as *P. gaudichaudi.* The species in this sense is distributed in Subarctic and Subantarctic regions.

Another hyperiid, *Hyperia spinigera,* has proved to be extremely elusive. It is still given specific status, but several systematists have doubted its claim to it. Stephensen (1942) writes: "This species is very uncertain, probably established on extremely developed large male of *H. galba,*" a view with which I agree. It differs from *galba* in the shape of the metasome segments and somewhat in the degree of setation of certain limb-joints and the shape of the uropods.

There are many other examples of this sort. All of them, "varieties," "species complexes," and yet unresolved difficult groups, are best considered as "morphs," to give final recognition to the fact that our concept of the "species" has not advanced very much in three centuries, and that we are dealing with a fluid situation which cannot be logically dealt with by means of a static classificatory system.

The term "morph" was proposed by Huxley (1955) to cover all cases of "balanced genetic polymorphism." To quote further from Huxley: "I

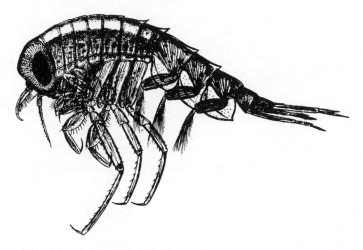

FIG. 18   *Parathemisto gaudichaudi, compressa* form. From Sars (1895).

restrict the term *morphism* to genetic polymorphism, as defined by Ford (1945), in which (usually sharply distinct) genetic variants or *morphs* coexist in temporary or permanent balance within a single interbreeding population in a single spatial region, and in such frequencies that the rarer cannot be due solely to mutation, or to the spread of selectively neutral mutants." This definition is intended to exclude geographical variants, although it is difficult to see how this can be done except in cases of full geographic isolation, which does not apply to the instances discussed here.

Many examples of morphism are reviewed or listed by Huxley, over and above those compiled by Bateson (1894) in his classic book, which is the starting point of Huxley's study. In both publications the great majority of examples are extra-tropical, most of them coming from cool temperate regions, and with the exception of the special case of mimicry, this is no doubt a true reflection of the actual situation, and is in keeping with the observation already made above that the difficulties of the systematist seem to bear a positive relation to geographic latitude, at least up to the southern boundary of the Arctic zone proper, north of which the number of species becomes very greatly reduced indeed.

The pattern that emerges, therefore, is one of a ferment of variability in northern regions, manifested by (1) anomalies in distribution, here in-

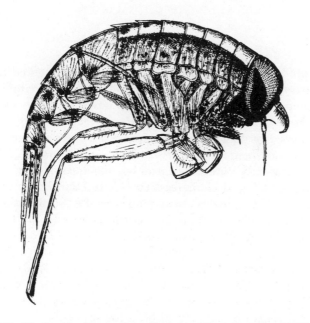

FIG. 19   *Parathemisto gaudichaudi, bispinosa* form. From Sars (1895).

terpreted as evidence of "cryptomorphs" involving physiological differences allowing for extensions of geographic distribution beyond the normal specific boundaries, (2) species complexes, as in the partially resolved case of *Calanus* spp. and the large number of genera still puzzling to the systematist, and (3) well-established dimorphic or polymorphic species. This pattern in turn implies a process of species formation and the consequent complication of the ecosystem. It is possible, furthermore, that the problem put forward by Bary (1963) can be eased by inclusion in this general pattern of variability. Bary finds that in order to interpret satisfactorily the distributions of certain marine zooplankton species, mainly copepods, in the North Atlantic, it becomes necessary to call for some unknown environmental factor other than temperature and salinity but in close association with those two parameters. I suggest that the unknown factors may be within the organisms and not in the environment, and that the anomalies of distribution may be explained by the existence within the specific populations of cryptomorphs whose tolerances extend beyond the typical specific limits.

It should be pointed out here that if this interpretation of distribution anomalies is correct, the plankton indicator technique becomes even more difficult to use than it is at present, for obvious reasons.

Ecosystem Development

Before the process of ecosystem development can be followed in detail, it will be necessary to know more about the precise distribution of the morphs concerned, but enough is already known to make a preliminary sketch. Of the several forms into which the former *Calanus finmarchicus* s. l. was separated by Yaschnov (1955), three are North Atlantic in distribution: *C. helgolandicus, C. finmarchicus* s. s., and *C. glacialis*. The ranges of the three forms have different centres but the areas of overlap are large. *C. helgolandicus* is found in the eastern North Atlantic roughly between latitudes 20° and 62°; *finmarchicus* ranges in the North Atlantic generally from latitude 40° northward into the Subarctic in the northeast (Barents Sea, Norwegian Sea), and northwest [Baffin Bay, Hudson Strait (Grainger 1963)]; *glacialis* is Arctic and Subarctic, extending southward in the west to the Gulf of Maine and the Iceland-Shetland region in the east. In the regions of overlap the two forms (*helgolandicus* does not overlap *glacialis*) may be and usually are found together in the same plankton hauls, and differences in size and in breeding season point to the sharing of the resources, presumably on Gausean lines (principle of exclusion). In West Greenland there is the possibility of the existence of yet another variant (Maclellan 1967) in the complex; and *Calanus hyperboreus,* another Arctic-Subarctic form not much more distinct morphologically from *glacialis* than *finmarchicus* is, should also be included in the group.

In *Thysanoessa inermis,* the present evidence suggests that the *neglecta* morph is rare in the Pacific (Hansen 1911, Banner 1949) and that it is not common in the Canadian eastern Arctic waters. It is, however, known from West Greenland, for instance in Disko Bay (Dunbar, unpublished). According to Hansen (1911) the elongated leg of *neglecta* is prehensile, with long curved naked setae on the sixth and seventh joints, much like the same legs in *T. longicaudata*. This, together with the divided eyes, suggest that this form is of raptorial and carnivorous habit, just as *longicaudata* is reported to be (Zelikman 1958), but there is a lack of direct evidence on this point in the form of stomach contents. *T. longicaudata* is also oceanic in preference, *inermis* neritic, so that it is possible that the "euphausid-carnivore" niche in the whole area is in process of being shared by *longicaudata* and *neglecta*.

As already mentioned, both Hansen (1911) and Einarsson (1945) reported that the immature stages of *inermis* very frequently, perhaps normally, are of the *neglecta* type, which might suggest that perhaps the food habit of the *inermis* type changes from carnivorous to herbivorous during development, and that the mature *neglecta* form constitutes a case of neoteny.

Thysanoessa inermis and *T. raschii* have very similar distributions, but there are differences in the tolerance to low temperature in the young, apparently, since *raschii* breeds in water of negative temperatures and *inermis* does not (Einarsson 1945). In consequence of this *raschii* is usually found farther east in the Barents Sea than is *inermis* (Drobysheva 1962), and the same authoress also gives some evidence for a climatic control of the annual abundance of the two species: "*T. inermis* dominait pendant des années chaudes et moyennes et la fréquence de *M. norvegica* était élevée; le pourcentage de *T. raschii* augmentait après des années froides." Despite this, the two species are frequently taken in the same plankton hauls and, as in the case of the *Calanus* species, their feeding habits are not known to be in any way different, with the possible exception of the *neglecta* form of *inermis,* as mentioned above. *T. raschii* is reported to favour shallower inshore areas than *inermis* (Einarsson 1945).

All specimens (sixteen in all) of *Parathemisto gaudichaudi* taken in Ungava Bay, during the "Calanus" expedition years in that area (1947–51), belonged to the *compressa* morph; and throughout Canadian waters, *compressa* seems to be the more common form, and to reach considerably farther north. In the southern hemisphere, both morphs are found together, but *bispinosa* "seems to be slightly more abundant, and also to prefer higher latitudes, not being found north of 41°S, whereas the former (*compressa*) was found about 34°S (off Cape Town)" (Barnard 1932). There is a third form in these southern waters (*thomsoni*) which is found in both *bispinosa* and *compressa,* distinguished by slight differences in the proportions of the segments of the first and second uropods. This constitutes a "sub-morph."

In the northern hemisphere generally, *P. gaudichaudi* is a Subarctic form, absent from the Pacific side entirely. The two morphs discussed here are reported by Stephensen (1923, 1942) to be more readily distinguishable in the northern than in the southern part of the range in the northern hemisphere; "in more southern waters the two [species] *T. com-*

pressa and *T. bispinosa* cannot always be separated with certainty, as they may combine characters of both" (Stephensen 1942). The two morphs have thus apparently diverged more, the one from the other, in the northern part of the range, an observation which is very relevant to the present discussion. According to Stephensen the distributions of the two forms in the northern hemisphere have a very large area in common. Both are found in the waters of northern Norway, the Murman coast, the Barents and Norwegian Seas, and in the Iceland and West Greenland regions.

Bigelow (1926), writing at a time when the two forms of *gaudichaudi* were considered to be separate species, discussed the distribution and relations between them in considerable detail. The relative abundance of the two morphs in the Gulf of Maine varied from season to season and from place to place, and *bispinosa* was found to be decidedly the more oceanic, or less neritic, of the two; the same has been reported from European waters.

Hyperia spinigera, suspected of being a morph of *H. galba,* is rare, having been recorded only from Spitsbergen, the north coast of Norway, Labrador, west of Ireland, the south coast of England, the Antarctic (Barnard 1932), and from Lake Harbour, Hudson Strait (Dunbar 1942).

This profusion of variation in temperate and Subarctic waters is to be interpreted, I suggest, as raw material for the process of ecosystem diversification and complication, leading to greater stability. The morphs described here are examples only; there are many others, and they appear to concentrate in extratropical regions, the tropics having developed mature, stable systems in which the limits of niche diversification and habitat-splitting have been reached. It remains now to study the process in greater detail, which will involve the plotting of exact distributions and changes in distribution with time, and divergence toward different food habits and other ecological demands on the part of the variant types. We have seen, for instance, that *T. raschii,* although it is normally found together with *T. inermis,* can breed in colder water and may prefer shallower regions. Do the two species also have different feeding habits? Do they breed at significantly different times of year? What are the ecological specializations of the *neglecta* form of *inermis?* Along the same line of enquiry, what are the functional differences, if any, between the two forms of *P. gaudichaudi,* and what are the precise ecological differences other than temperature preferences between the members of the *Calanus* group? Is complete geographic isolation necessary before effective speciation can occur?

Whatever the answers to these questions, the conclusion seems inescapable that the large number of morphs in high latitudes implies ecosystem development, which in turn means that the present patterns, although they may appear in the short term to be in equilibrium, are immature and still in process of growth. Such growth in complexity is to be expected on theoretical grounds, and there are many ways in which it could be accomplished, of which adaptation to low temperature is probably the least important and the simplest to achieve.

Chapter 8

REHEARSAL AND DISCUSSION

Arguments and evidence have been marshalled in the past seven chapters, especially in Chapters 2 and 4, to show that the low temperature of the polar regions is the least important of the various polar characteristics in estimating and understanding Arctic and Subarctic life and living systems. Low temperatures on land enforce certain special adaptations for winter tolerance or avoidance, such as dormancy and migration, and in both land and sea environments temperature is important in determining the limits of distribution of species at the present time, which is an effect strictly at the proximate level. It is also an important factor in determining the length of the growing season on land, and hence may be involved in the limitation of production, again on land; in the sea it does not appear to be a limiting factor on production as defined here.

The climatic change which appears to have begun some time in the Pliocene, and which has given rise to the present polar condition, can best be understood as being the result of a shift in the positions of the geographic poles from former positions in open oceanic circulations to their present positions in a contained marine area (Arctic Ocean) and a continent (Antarctica). In the Arctic, the polar shift and climatic change have produced low temperatures, high vertical stability in the water column in the Arctic Ocean and consequent low production, and a highly oscillating nutrient supply for plants and plant food supply for animals. The Antarctic effects are low temperatures and very high marine production in the waters surrounding the polar continent. These effects have been described in Chapter 4. Light conditions are similar at both poles: a light-rich summer and a light-poor winter, but the Antarctic winter night falls on ice-covered land. Finally, the Pleistocene, in which we now live, is an epoch of oscillating climate from glacial to interglacial. The Pleistocene as such, defined by various means (Chapter 3), has lasted for a length of time which is at present still quite uncertain, with estimates ranging from three or four million years to 300,000, and the date of the beginning of the last ice recession lies somewhere in the region of 15,000 years ago. This recession has not been complete and probably has never been complete in Pleistocene time.

The evolution of life in these conditions, and the development of high latitude ecosystems, have been presented as manifesting two somewhat conflicting processes involving two "goals" (it is now once more permissible to talk of goals in evolutionary biology): (1) adaptation of the system to the oscillating environment and (2) adaptation, or evolution, towards greater ecosystem stability. The former process seems to be well advanced, the latter much less so, but there is evidence that it is under way. It is in this latter process, therefore, that much of the interest lies, and in this final chapter I propose to develop the discussion of it and to consider what sort of selection it involves.

There are several ecological factors which encourage or favour increase in specific diversity (number of species in the system), according to present ecological theory. These are (1) climatic stability, (2) habitat variety (spatial heterogeneity), (3) large biomass (high production), (4) high productivity, or the rate of energy flow through the system, (5) predation, (6) competition, and (7) time. These seven determinants form the conditions in which new niches are formed by the appearance of new variants whose properties (food habits, time of activity, time of breeding, size, and so on) can be accepted into the system harmoniously. By this means the system grows in complexity and hence in stability. What we must do, therefore, is to examine these conditions as they are found in polar regions.

Climate

The principle of the "sharing of the energy" (see Chapter 2) has been variously developed by different authors. Connell and Orias (1964), whose paper has been fully treated in Chapter 5, write: "with a more stable environment fewer or less severe challenges will be presented to the organisms in that ecosystem, and therefore, less regulatory activity will be required of them. Therefore, more of the assimilated energy will be channelled into productivity, that is, growth and production of offspring." Thus stable climates give larger specific populations and therefore more variable populations, hence more active speciation. This in fact is not what is found in the tropics, where stable climate is associated with lesser specific productivity, not greater. Cody (1966), discussing clutch size in birds, takes a different approach, emphasizing that in the higher latitudes the carrying capacity of the environment for a given species is often not realized owing to periodic local catastrophes; hence "any phenotypic variation which enables parents to leave more offspring will be selected for." In the tropics, on the other hand, according to this view, populations are normally at saturation densities, so that clutch size can be smaller and more energy spent in other activities, such as predator avoidance, care of the young, and intraspecific competition designed to increase the carrying capacity by increasing the efficiency of the use of resources.

There are certain objections to be raised to both these theories. To begin with, to talk of the sharing of the available energy is to skate on very thin ice; it appears to assume that organisms are closed systems and that only a certain quantity of energy is available for the lifetime of each individual. It was offered in Chapter 2 only as a general way of looking on certain problems of metabolism, activity, growth, and reproduction in Arctic poikilotherms, and it was put forward somewhat tentatively. It has not been demonstrated that organisms do in fact behave in this way, and it would be difficult to do so. Moreover there is much that strongly suggests the contrary. Many birds and some insects spend a great deal of energy on migratory flights of some hundreds and even thousands of miles, twice a year; yet these are among the species which produce the largest numbers of eggs, there being a very good positive correlation in most groups between clutch size and geographic latitude. Again, many organisms become dormant in the polar winter, by a variety of means, thus reducing their energy requirement to close to zero when the available environmental energy is also extremely low; during the polar summer there is energy in abundance. Thirdly, other activities besides the production of young are calculated to raise or maintain the population level, such as predator avoidance and the achievement of more efficient use of resources, and they would therefore be advantageous in all climates, stable or unstable. Finally, the idea that greater predation pressure on the young, which is apparently much greater in tropical than in temperate environments (Cody 1966), would favour greater development of predator avoidance is questionable. It should also favour the production of large numbers of offspring; whether the population is reduced by climatic hazards or by predation is not the main point, since the population is reduced by either means. The equivalent development to be expected in higher latitudes is greater efficiency in avoiding or surviving the climatic hazards, which on the "energy sharing" principle would require a reduction in clutch size.

It seems that the best explanation of the correlation between clutch size and geographic latitude is still the simplest, namely that put forward by Lack (1954), who relates the clutch size to the available food supply and the daylight hours which can be used in feeding the young. Food supply is limiting in the tropics as it presumably is also in other areas, but in the temperate and polar regions there is not only a very large food supply in the spring and summer, but also a smaller number of species to share it at the present stage of the evolution of the faunas.

Clutch size in birds is of course only one of the many sides to the question. In the marine plankton the same rule appears to hold, that the egg production is lower in tropical waters than elsewhere, and the same arguments may well apply to them. In the benthos, especially the sessile species, the reverse appears to be true (Thorson 1950), except possibly for those few species that have retained the planktonic larvae (see Chapter 2). The tendency in the benthos generally in the northern regions is to produce few large eggs rather than many small eggs, and to extend the possible time of spawning over a large part of the year, or over the whole year; in these cases climatic oscillation appears to have no influence at all. In the fishes, Marshall (1953) has brought together evidence of a similar low egg production in Arctic fishes, and Downes (1964) points out that in at least some groups of insects (blackflies, bumblebees, and probably aphids) the egg production in the Arctic is significantly lower than it is farther south. With respect to the "hazards of the Arctic" discussed above, Downes writes: "The very small egg-number must indicate that these insects are well adapted to the environment and no longer exposed to large irregular risks."

It is thus possible to doubt that the seasonal climatic instability of the higher latitudes has any direct bearing on the development of the productivity or the diversity of the ecosystem, except perhaps in one aspect which applies to the land rather than to the sea, namely the winter conditions in the Arctic, in which the temperature drops below possible activity levels for poikilotherms and thus eliminates from the total "hypervolume" available for exploitation a considerable proportion of the time dimension. In the sea the climatic seasonal instability is in fact quite small, the differences between summer and winter temperatures being apparent only in the upper water and largely in the temperate rather than the Arctic regions.

The climatic instability discussed here should not be confused with the seasonal environmental oscillation discussed in Chapters 5 and 6; that environmental oscillation is one of nutrient supply and hence of plant food, and is related only in part and indirectly to the climatic oscillation as such, especially in the sea.

Climatic instability can have longer periods than the diurnal and the annual. Short-term climatic change within an interglacial period probably offers no serious problems to biological systems; distribution ranges change somewhat, but the systems as wholes remain the same. The longer-term changes, however, representing the ebb and flow between full glacial and maximum interglacial within the Pleistocene framework, are obviously decisive in terrestrial (as opposed to marine) environments, and in marine environments, problematical. We may take it that so long as the geographic poles of the earth remain where they are, so long in fact as they remain in a contained ocean and on a large continent respectively, the present Pleistocene conditions will continue. It was pointed out earlier that the term "Recent," applied to the time since the last ice recession, is misleading and probably the result of wishful thinking. The ice sheets over northern lands will return unless mankind by that time has become sufficiently skilled a geomorphic force to keep them at bay. Another glacial period would remove all life from the land of most of northern North America and northwestern Europe, as before, so that in the period between now and then the living systems of the land in those sensitive areas have only a few thousand years in which to develop to greater maturity, after which they will be removed and must start again in the next interglacial.

The probable effects on the marine conditions are by no means clear. Ewing and Donn, in papers already quoted, have speculated that the Arctic Ocean would be ice-free during part of the Pleistocene climatic oscillation; certainly there is no apparent reason to suppose that any such drastic effects would be felt in the sea as would be inevitable on the land, and if this is so then the living systems of the high latitude seawaters have had in the past, and will have in the future, a great deal longer time of continued existence in their present positions.

Habitat Variety

The growth of habitat diversity is a complicated geological, pedological, botanical, and zoological process involving many feedback loops. Smooth rock gives way to weathering and the working of lichens; pockets of coarse soil form, in which pioneer plants grow and increase the humus content; spiders and insects colonize the soil; these processes continue on substrates of different chemical natures until trees grow and larger animals invade the area. By this stage the momentum of growth is considerable, and continues to the rain forest climax in warm humid regions. The pattern becomes complicated further by changes in the surfaces of the continents, the sinking and uplifting of continental margins and mountain ranges, and the formation of new lakes and marshes. As new species of plants appear, the habitat complexity for animals increases, and new animal species open the way for new plants and new animals, and the soil capital continues to grow. The most important ingredient is time. Furthermore, the process is reversible, for uplifting or large climatic cooling can extinguish species and even whole systems, and erosion will set the growth process back to an earlier stage.

The same processes go on in the sea, but with the obvious differences. The vertical dimension is greater, but similarity of light conditions, the enormous volumes involved, and the unifying process of sedimentation put a lower limit on the possibilities for habitat diversification in the sea than on land; this limit is reflected in the fact that some 80 per cent of animal species are terrestrial, and only 20 per cent marine. In shallow water and in the intertidal zone, however, diversification is indeed possible and in tropical and subtropical regions has grown to rival the rain forest itself.

Within large limits, habitat development both on land and in the sea will continue irrespective of the direction of climatic change at any given time and place. For instance, the northward creep of the tree line which has been reported both in Scandinavia and in Canada has usually been ascribed to the climatic upswing of the past fifty years. This is a doubtful correlation, for the process of soil increment would continue even though the climate were cooling, so that the continued northward march of the trees is to be expected in any event. Only the reappearance of the glacial ice sheets will stop it. Habitat diversification can in fact be expected to continue in northern regions, and therefore will continue to favour general ecological stabilization, except in certain special situations.

Habitat diversification is not to be expected in the Arctic intertidal, where the substrates are continually scraped by ice during a large part of the year. The conspicuous poverty of the Arctic intertidal fauna bears witness to this handicap. In shallow water, and perhaps generally over Arctic and Antarctic sea floors, the high rate of deposition of glacial silt must limit the habitat potential, but perhaps not much more so than in other seas, where other types of sediment are dominant over very large areas.

One locus of spatial heterogeneity which is specific to the polar seas and whose existence has only recently been appreciated is the sea ice itself. Bunt (in press), studying the biota of sea ice, has pointed out that the sea ice offers a remarkably nonhomogeneous environment, a fact that is supported by recent studies on the physical nature of the ice. In regions where habitat variety is scarce, and perhaps especially in the sea, this is an ecological opportunity not to be missed, and it is clear that it has already been exploited not inconsiderably by plant populations; little is known as yet about animal populations associated with the plants, although some advances have been made in the Arctic (Barnard 1959, English 1961). Bunt has been working in the Antarctic.

Biomass and Productivity

The *biomass* is the total amount of living substance in a system at any given time, and is therefore related to the "production" as the term is used in this book; both form part of the total energy capital of the system, with the rest of the energy being represented in nonliving phases. *Productivity,* on the other hand, as the term is usually used by ecologists today, is defined as the rate at which living substance is formed, and is thus a measure of energy flow through the system (that is, of turnover). Large biomass and high production, since they reflect high energy capital, lead to community stability by making possible specific diversification and the sharing of the resources by many species. It has already been established that production is high in the tropical rain forest, in certain unstable areas in tropical seas, in Antarctic waters, and in temperate and Subarctic regions; it is low in the Arctic Ocean and over the very large areas of stable tropical and subtropical seas, but there is clearly more to be learnt about these warm-water regions in this respect, for despite low production the species diversity is high.

The annual production in coral reefs, moreover, appears to be remarkably high (Westlake 1963). The rate of turnover in the rain forest is uncertain, but since production is high it has been assumed that the rate of production is also high, which is not necessarily so. Productivity is high in temperate and Subarctic regions during the growing season, both on land and in the sea, and it is high in Antarctic waters.

The orthodox view today is that both large biomass and high productivity favour ecological diversity and hence stability, and that if either biomass or productivity is held constant and the other increased, stability increases. This has been questioned, however, in a very interesting paper by Leigh (1965), who by mathematical argument (only part of which the present writer was able to follow) concludes that "an increase in productivity for fixed biomass, or a decrease in biomass for fixed productivity, increases the turnover rate and thus decreases stability." This is a difficult conclusion to accept intuitively, but it points to the need for a re-examination of the hydrographically stable tropical oceanic regions in which biomass is low, ecological stability and diversity are both high, and there is controversy concerning the turnover rate.

Predation and Competition

Predation, by keeping the most abundant species in control, permits the rarer species to survive, according to present theory; and competition, by favouring increased specialization in the use of the total resources, allows the establishment of new species. These apply in the polar regions as any-where else, and little comment is called for. The relevance of morphologi-cal and physiological variants to the increase in species number by more specialized use of resources has already been pointed out in Chapter 7.

Time

There is no argument over the different ages of the tropical and polar climates, nor over the importance of time in achieving ecological satura-tion. The question to be resolved is whether enough time has elapsed since the Pliocene-Pleistocene climatic change to allow ecological satura-tion to have been reached in the high latitudes, that is, whether the eco-logical systems of the polar and subpolar regions are in fact saturated.

The demonstration of evolution in process is always difficult, pre-cisely because of the time factor. Except perhaps in special isolated en-vironments with simple systems, such as islands, little more can be done than to present suggestions and patterns of probability; the rest is an act of faith. In Chapters 6 and 7, evidence of this sort was marshalled to pre-sent a pattern of evolution in progress toward greater diversification in northern ecosystems; the evidence was taken entirely from the marine biota. It cannot be conclusive evidence. Thus the fact that photosynthesis can continue under the ice at very low light intensities, or that many of the marine invertebrates produce their young in the winter, may well sig-nify no more than that these particular adaptations have occurred, are established, and will progress no further. Yet they are suggestive in that they can be interpreted as steps toward the extension of the period of primary production and the spreading of the use of resources over a larger part of the year. Two-phase or polyphase breeding cycles, in which each individual breeds only once, produce a condition in which sympatric speciation becomes possible, perhaps probable. The prevalence of mor-phological and physiological variants within species in Subarctic and temperate regions is more direct evidence, offering a pattern of active speciation; and the same is true of the species complexes which have been quoted. Such developments in fact present step-clines, acknowledged to be indicative of ecological unsaturation. The oscillating nature of the high latitude systems, although possibly immediately referable to the os-cillation in the food supply, leads one to expect changes which will damp the oscillations. This may be more difficult on land than in the sea, be-cause of the decisive discouragement of the Arctic winter; in the sea this extreme condition does not exist.

Bramlette (1965) comments on the time required, according to the fossil record, to produce ecological diversification after the massive extinctions that have occurred in the past. Discussing extinctions that took place at the end of Mesozoic time, he writes that "it required several million years also for the meager assemblages of the nannoplankton and plank-tonic foraminifera surviving into the earliest Cenozoic to develop diversi-fication comparable to that found in the late Mesozoic." The fossil record gives the same information for many other groups of organisms. It took many millions of years for the amphibian fauna to develop to significant diversification in the Devonian, similarly for the reptiles in the Permian and the birds from the Jurassic onward. In the face of this evidence it does not seem reasonable to suppose that diversification in temperate and polar regions has achieved saturation since the Pliocene-Pleistocene cli-matic change. The issue here is not whether enough time has elapsed to reach saturation and maximum stability in the polar regions, but rather what degrees of diversification and stability are possible under polar con-ditions; the position taken in this short discussion of the problem is, in effect, that the growth of diversification is in its infancy.

By way of a *coda,* it might be worth adding that we have been look-ing at evolution in the polar regions as an ecological problem, which in-deed it is, and have emphasized the development of the ecosystem as a whole rather than the evolution of individual species within the system. Once this point of view is taken, it is tempting to wonder whether nat-ural selection may not operate at levels higher than that of the individual; that is, whether it is possible for ecosystems, defined as may be convenient, to act as units of selection. This idea was tentatively developed in an ear-lier paper (Dunbar 1960), and received a somewhat mixed reception, some being quite enthusiastic, others not so. The contrary criticism pointed out that selection between ecosystems toward greater stability amounted to the demand for an "altruism" in the selective process at the individual level which produced great difficulties in theory. These difficulties do not seem to me to be insurmountable, and it is possible that we have become rather narrow-minded in our Darwin-Mendel tradition of individual se-lection. But this is a highly complicated matter, and not one which di-rectly affects the thesis of this book; it seems wisest, therefore, to follow the example of Poincaré, to fold up the manuscript and "think about this some more."

REFERENCES

Allee, W. C., A. E. Emerson, O. Park, T. Park, and K. P. Schmidt, 1949. Principles of Animal Ecology. Philadelphia & London: W. B. Saunders Co.; 837 pp.

Allen, J. A., 1877. The influence of physical conditions in the genesis of species. Radical Rev., 1: 108–140.

Apollonio, S., 1961. The chlorophyll content of Arctic sea ice. Arctic, 14 (3): 197–199.

Arrhenius, G., 1952. Sediment cores from the East Pacific. Rep. Swedish Deep Sea Expedition, 1947–48, 5 (1): 1–227.

Arrhenius, S., 1915. Quantitative Laws in Biological Chemistry. London: Bell.

Baker, J. R., 1938. The evolution of breeding seasons. In: G. R. de Beer (Ed.); Evolution: 161–177, Oxford: Clarendon Press.

Banner, A. H., 1949. A taxonomic study of the Mysidacea and Euphausiacea (Crustacea) of the North Pacific. Pt. III; Euphausiacea. Trans. Roy. Can. Inst., 28 (58): 2–49.

Barghoorn, E. S., 1953. Evidence of climatic change in the geologic record of plant life. In: Shapley, H. (Ed.); Climatic Change: 235–248, Cambridge, Mass.: Harvard Univ. Press.

Barnard, J. L., 1958. Index to the families, genera, and species of the Gammaridean Amphipoda (Crustacea). Allan Hancock Foundation Publications, occasional paper No. 19: 1–141.

Barnard, J. L., 1959. Epipelagic and under-ice Amphipoda of the Central Arctic Basin. Geophysical Research Papers No. 63, Scientific Studies at Fletcher's Ice Island, T-3 (1952–1955), Vol. I: 115–152.

Barnard, K. H., 1932. Amphipoda. Discovery Reports, 5: 1–326.

Bary, B. M., 1963. Distribution of Atlantic pelagic organisms in relation to surface water bodies. In: Dunbar, M. J. (Ed.); Marine Distributions: 51–67, Univ. of Toronto Press.

101

Bateson, W., 1894. Materials for the Study of Variation. London: Macmillan & Co.; 598 pp.

Bělehrádek, J., 1935. Temperature and Living Matter. Protoplasma-Monogr. 8: Berlin, 229 pp.

Berg, K., 1953. The problem of respiratory acclimatization. Hydrobiologica, 5 (4): 331–350.

Bergmann, C., 1847. Ueber die Verhältnisse der Wärmeökonomie der Thiere zu ihrer Grösse. Göttinger Studien, 3: 595–708.

Bertram, G. C. L., 1935. The low temperature limit of activity of Arctic insects. J. Anim. Ecol., 4: 35–42.

Bigelow, H. B., 1926. Plankton of the Gulf of Maine. Bull. U.S. Bur. Fish. Doc. 968, Vol. 40: 1–509.

Bliss, L. C., 1962. Adaptations of Arctic and alpine plants to environmental conditions. Arctic, 15: 117–144.

Bogorov, B. G., 1940. On the biology of the Euphausiidae and Chaetognatha in the Barents Sea. Bull. de la Société des Naturalistes de Moscou, N.S., XLIX (2): 3–18.

Bramlette, M. N., 1965. Massive extinctions in biota at the end of Mesozoic time. Science, 148 (3678): 1696–1699.

Bray, J. R., 1962. Zoogeography and systematics of Isopoda of the Beaufort Sea. McGill Univ. thesis: 138 pp. (MS).

Brodskii, K. A. and M. N. Nikitin, 1955. Hydrobiological work. Observational Data of the Scientific Research Drifting Station of 1950–1951, 1, Sec. 4, Art. 7:32 pp. (Amer. Met. Soc. Translation).

Bruun, A. F. and T. Wolff, 1961. Abyssal benthic organisms: nature, origin, distribution, and influence on sedimentation. In: Mary Sears (Ed.); Oceanography: 391–397. Washington; A.A.A.S.

Bullock, T. H., 1955. Compensation for temperature in metabolism and activity of poikilotherms. Biol. Rev., 30: 311–342.

Bunt, J. S., 1963. Diatoms of Antarctic sea ice as agents of primary production. Nature, 199: 1255–1257.

Bunt, J. S., 1964. Primary productivity under sea ice in Antarctic waters. I. Concentrations and photosynthetic activities of microalgae in the waters of McMurdo Sound, Antarctica. Antarctic Res. Ser., 1: 13–26. Amer. Geophysical Union.

Bunt, J. S., in press. Microalgae of the Antarctic pack ice zone. SCAR–SCOR–IAPO–IUBS Symposium on Antarctic Oceanography, Santiago, Chile, September 1966.

Bunt, J. S. and E. J. F. Wood, 1963. Microalgae and Antarctic sea ice. Nature, 199: 1254.

Bursa, A. S., 1961. The annual oceanographic cycle at Igloolik in the Canadian Arctic. II. The Phytoplankton. J. Fish. Res. Bd. Canada, 18 (4): 563–615.

Burton, A. C. and O. G. Edholm, 1955. Man in a Cold Environment. London: Edward Arnold Ltd.; 273 pp.

Cairns, A. A., 1965. The life cycle of *Pseudocalanus minutus* (Kröyer) in Tanquary Fiord, Ellesmere Island. McGill University Thesis: 56 pp.

Cody, M. L., 1966. A general theory of clutch size. Evolution, 20 (2): 174–184.

Connell, J. H. and E. Orias, 1964. The ecological regulation of species diversity. Amer. Nat., XCVIII (903): 399–414.

Conover, R. J., 1959. Regional and seasonal variation in the respiratory rate of marine copepods. Limnol. & Oceanogr., 4: 259–268.

Conover, R. J., 1960. The feeding, behavior and respiration of some marine planktonic Crustacea. Biol. Bull., 119: 399–415.

Conover, R. J., 1962. Metabolism and growth in *Calanus hyperboreus* in relation to its life cycle. Conseil Permanent: Rapp. et Proc. Verb., 153: 190–197.

Damon, P. E., 1965. Pleistocene time scales. Science, 148 (3673): 1037–1038.

Dampier, W. C., 1957. A Shorter History of Science. New York: Meridian Books; 190 pp.

Dansereau, Pierre, 1955. Biogeography of the land and inland waters. In: Kimble and Good (Eds.); Geography of the Northlands: 84–118. New York: Amer. Geogr. Soc.

Dehnel, P. A., 1955. Rates of growth of gastropods as a function of latitude. Physiol. Zool., 28 (2): 115–144.

Demeusy, N., 1957. Respiratory metabolism of the fiddler crab *Uca pugilator* from two different latitudinal populations. Biol. Bull., 113: 245–253.

Digby, P. S. B., 1954. The biology of the marine planktonic copepods of Scoresby Sound, East Greenland. J. Anim. Ecol., 23 (2): 298–338.

Donn, W. L. and M. Ewing, 1966. A theory of ice ages III. Science, 152 (3730): 1706–1712.

Dorf, E., 1960. Climatic changes of the past and present. Amer. Sci., 48 (3): 364.

Downes, J. A., 1964. Arctic insects and their environment. Canadian Entomologist, 96: 279–307.

Drobysheva, S. S., 1957. The effect of some aspects of the biology of the Euphausiacea upon the summer feeding conditions for cod in the Barents Sea.

Trudy Poliarnovo N. I. Inst. Morskovo Rybnovo Khoziaistva i Okeanografii (PINRO), 10: 106–124.

Drobysheva, S. S., 1962. Les conditions biologiques du prognostic du stock des euphausides dans la partie sud de la mer de Barents. I.C.E.S. (Comité du Plancton), No. 110 (MS).

Dunbar, M. J., 1940. On the size distribution and breeding cycles of four marine planktonic animals from the Arctic. J. Anim. Ecol., 9 (2): 215–226.

Dunbar, M. J., 1941. The breeding cycle in *Sagitta elegans arctica* Aurivillius. Can. J. Research, D 19 (9): 258–266.

Dunbar, M. J., 1942. Marine macroplankton from the Canadian eastern Arctic. I. Amphipoda and Schizopoda. Can. J. Research, D 20: 33–46.

Dunbar, M. J., 1946a. On *Themisto libellula* in Baffin Island coastal waters. J. Fish. Res. Bd. Canada, 6 (6): 419–434.

Dunbar, M. J., 1946b. The state of the West Greenland current up to 1944. J. Fish. Res. Bd. Canada, VI (7): 460–471.

Dunbar, M. J., 1954. The Amphipod Crustacea of Ungava Bay, Canadian eastern Arctic. J. Fish. Res. Bd. Canada, 11 (6): 709–798.

Dunbar, M. J., 1957. The determinants of production in northern seas: A study of the biology of *Themisto libellula* Mandt. Can. J. Zool., 35 (6): 797–819.

Dunbar, M. J., 1958. Physical oceanographic results of the "Calanus" Expeditions in Ungava Bay, Frobisher Bay, Cumberland Sound, Hudson Strait and Northern Hudson Bay, 1949–1955. J. Fish. Res. Bd. Can., 15 (2): 155–201.

Dunbar, M. J., 1960. The evolution of stability in marine environments; natural selection at the level of the ecosystem. Amer. Nat., XCIV (875), 129–136.

Dunbar, M. J., 1962. The life cycle of *Sagitta elegans* in Arctic and Subarctic seas, and the modifying effects of hydrographic differences in the environment. J. Mar. Res., 20 (1): 76–91.

Dunbar, M. J., 1963. Ecological adaptation to the glacial climate. Trans. Roy. Soc. Canada, I (Ser. IV): 433–440.

Dunbar, M. J., 1964. Euphausids and pelagic amphipods: Distribution in North Atlantic and Arctic waters. Serial Atlas Marine Environment, Folio 6: 2 pp. plus 8 maps.

Einarsson, H., 1945. Euphausiacea: I. Northern Atlantic species. Carlsberg Foundation, Dana-Report No. 27: 185 pp.

Eiseley, L., 1963. Man: the lethal factor. Amer. Sci., 51 (1): 71–83.

Ekman, S., 1953. Zoogeography of the Sea. London: Sidgwick & Jackson; 417 pp.

El-Sayed, S. Z., E. Mandelli, and Y. Sugimura, 1964. Primary organic production in the Drake Passage and Bransfield Strait. Antarctic Res. Ser., 1: 1–11. Amer. Geophysical Union.

Elton, C., 1927. Animal Ecology. London: Sidgwick & Jackson; 207 pp.

Elton, C., 1930. Animal Ecology and Evolution. Oxford: Clarendon Press; 96 pp.

Emiliani, C., 1961. Cenozoic climatic changes as indicated by the stratigraphy and chronology of deep-sea cores of globigerina-ooze facies. Ann. N.Y. Acad. Sci., 95 (1): 521–536.

English, T. S., 1959. Primary production in the central North Polar Sea; Drifting Station Alpha, 1957–58. Arctic Inst. N. Amer., M.S. report; 22 pp. & app.

English, T. S., 1961. Some biological oceanographical observations in the central North Polar Sea; Drift Station Alpha, 1957–58. Arctic Inst. N. Amer.: Research Paper No. 13; 79 pp.

Ericson, D. B., 1959. Coiling direction of Globigerina pachyderma as a climatic index. Science, 130 (3369): 219–220.

Ericson, D. B., M. Ewing, and G. Wollin, 1963. Pliocene-Pleistocene boundary in deep-sea sediments. Science, 139 (3556): 727–737.

Ewing, M. and W. L. Donn, 1956. A theory of ice ages. Science, 123: 1061–1066.

Ewing, M. and W. L. Donn, 1958. A theory of ice ages II. Science, 127 (3307): 1159–1162.

Ewing, M. and W. L. Donn, 1960. On Pleistocene surface temperatures of the North Atlantic and Arctic Oceans. Science, 131 (3393): 99.

Ewing, M. and W. L. Donn, 1964. Polar wandering and climate. In: Polar Wandering and Continental Drift: 94–99. Soc. Econ. Paleontologists and Mineralogists.

Fairbridge, R. W., 1961. Convergence of evidence on climatic change and ice ages. Ann. N.Y. Acad. Sci., 95 (1): 542–579.

Ferguson-Wood, E. J., 1965. Marine Microbial Ecology. London: Chapman & Hall; 243 pp.

Fischer, A. G., 1960. Latitudinal variations in organic diversity. Evolution, XIV (1): 64–81.

Fontaine, M., 1955. The planktonic copepods (Calanoida, Cyclopoida, Monstrilloida) of Ungava Bay, with special reference to the biology of Pseudocalanus minutus and Calanus finmarchicus. J. Fish. Res. Bd. Canada, 12 (6): 858–898.

Ford, E. B., 1945. Polymorphism. Biol. Rev., 20: 73–88.

Fox, H. Munro, 1936. The activity and metabolism of poikilothermal animals in different latitudes, I. Proc. Zool. Soc. Lond., 1936: 945–955.

Fox, H. Munro, 1938. The activity and metabolism of poikilothermal animals in different latitudes, III. Proc. Zool. Soc: Lond., Ser. A, 1938: 501–505.

Fox, H. Munro, 1939. The activity and metabolism of poikilothermal animals in different latitudes–V. Proc. Zool. Soc. Lond., Ser. A, 1939: 141–156.

Fox, H. Munro and C. A. Wingfield, 1937. The activity and metabolism of poikilothermal animals in different latitudes, II. Proc. Zool. Soc. Lond., Ser. A., 1937: 275–282.

Fry, F. E. J., 1951. Some environmental relations of the speckled trout (*Salvelinus fontinalis*). Proc. N. E. Atl. Fish. Conf., 1951: 1–29.

Fry, F. E. J., 1958. Temperature compensation. Ann. Rev. Physiol., 20: 207–220.

Grainger, E. H., 1953. On the age, growth, migration, reproductive potential and feeding habits of the Arctic char (*Salvelinus alpinus*) of Frobisher Bay, Baffin Island. J. Fish. Res. Bd. Canada, 10 (6): 326–370.

Grainger, E. H., 1959. The annual oceanographic cycle at Igloolik in the Canadian Arctic. 1. The zooplankton and physical and chemical observations. J. Fish. Res. Bd. Canada, 16 (4): 453–501.

Grainger, E. H., 1962. Zooplankton of Foxe Basin in the Canadian Arctic. J. Fish. Res. Bd. Canada, 19 (3): 377–400.

Gurjanova, E., 1951. Gammaridea of the seas of the U.S.S.R. and adjacent waters. Tabl. Anal. Fauna URSS, No. 41: 1–1032.

Hammen, Th. van der, 1961. Upper Cretaceous and Tertiary climatic periodicities and their causes. Ann. N.Y. Acad. Sci., 95 (1): 440–448.

Hansen, H. J., 1911. The genera and species of the order Euphausiacea. Bull. Inst. Océanogr. Monaco. No. 210.

Hartley, C. H. and M. J. Dunbar, 1938. On the hydrographic mechanism of the so-called brown zones associated with tidal glaciers. J. Mar. Res., 1 (4): 305–311.

Harvey, H. W., 1957. The Chemistry and Fertility of Sea Waters. Cambridge Univ. Press: 2nd ed.; 228 pp.

Haviland, M. D., 1926. Forest, Steppe & Tundra. Cambridge Univ. Press; 218 pp.

Hesse, R., W. C. Allee, and K. P. Schmidt, 1951. Ecological Animal Geography. New York: Wiley; 715 pp.

Hildebrand, H. H., 1948. Marine fishes of Arctic Canada. McGill University thesis (MS).

Hildebrand, H. H., 1949. Notes on *Rana sylvatica* in the Labrador Peninsula. Copeia, 1949 (3): 168–172.

Hildebrand, H. H., n.d. Marine fishes of the North American Arctic. Encyclopedia Arctica, III, Pt. II, No. 6: 19 pp. (Mimeogr.)

Hjort, J. and J. T. Ruud, 1938. Deep sea prawn fisheries and their difficulties. Hvalrådets Skr., Nr. 17: 1–144.

Hutchinson, G. E., 1953. Patterns in ecology. Proc. Acad. Nat. Sci., Philadelphia, 105: 1–12.

Hutchinson, G. E., 1957. Concluding remarks. Cold Spring Harbor Symp. on Quantitative Biol., 22: 415–427.

Hutchinson, G. E., 1959. Homage to Santa Rosalia, or, Why are there so many kinds of animals? Amer. Nat., 93 (870): 145–159.

Huxley, J. S., 1955. Morphism and evolution. Heredity, 9 (1): 1–52.

ICNAF, 1953. Contributions to a special meeting on long-term hydrographic changes. ICNAF Ann. Proc., 3: 67–86.

ICNAF, 1965. Effects of long-term trends. ICNAF Spec. Publ., No. 6: 791–858.

Jensen, Ad. S., 1939. Concerning a change of climate during recent decades in the Arctic and Subarctic regions, from Greenland in the west to Eurasia in the east, and contemporary biological and geophysical changes. Det Kgl. Danske Vidensk. Selsk., Biologiske Meddelelser, 14 (8): 1–75.

Kimble, G. H. T. and D. Good (Eds.), 1955. Geography of the Northlands. New York: Amer. Geogr. Soc. and Wiley; 534 pp.

King, C. E., 1964. Relative abundance of species and MacArthur's model. Ecology, 45 (4): 716–727.

Klopfer, P. H. and R. H. MacArthur, 1960. Niche size and faunal diversity. Amer. Nat., 94: 293–300.

Klopfer, P. H. and R. H. MacArthur, 1961. On the causes of tropical species diversity: niche overlap. Amer. Nat., XCV (883): 223–226.

Krehl, L. and F. Soetbeer, 1899. Untersuchungen über die Temperaturabhängigkeit von Lebensprozessen bei verschiedenen Wirbellosen. Pflüg. Arch. ges. Physiol. 77: 611.

Krogh, A., 1916. Respiratory Exchange of Animals and Man. London: Longmans, Green.

Kusunoki, K., 1962. Hydrography of the Arctic Ocean with special reference to the Beaufort Sea. Contr. Inst. Low Temp. Sci., Ser A. No. 17: 1–74.

Lack, D., 1954. The Natural Regulation of Animal Numbers. Oxford: Clarendon Press; 343 pp.

Leicester, H. M., 1956. The Historical Background of Chemistry. New York: Wiley; London: Chapman and Hall; 260 pp.

Leigh, E. G., 1965. On the relation between the productivity, biomass, diversity, and stability of a community. Proc. Nat. Acad. Sci., 53 (4): 777–783.

Lindroth, C. H., 1963. The problem of late land connections in the North Atlantic area. In: Löve and Löve (Eds.); North Atlantic Biota: 73–85. New York: Pergamon Press.

Loeb, Jacques, 1908. Über den Temperaturkoeffizienten für die Lebensdauer kaltblütiger Thiere und über die Ursache des natürlichen Todes. Pflügers Archiv f. die ges. Physiol., 124: 411–426.

Löve, A. and D. Löve, 1956. Cytotaxonomical conspectus of the Icelandic flora. Acta Horti Gotob., 20: 1–291.

MacArthur, R. H., 1955. Fluctuations of animal populations, and a measure of community stability. Ecology, 36: 533–536.

MacArthur, R. H., 1957. On the relative abundance of bird species. Proc. Nat. Acad. Sci., 43: 293–295.

MacArthur, R. H., 1960. On the relative abundance of species. Amer. Nat., 94: 25–36.

Macdonald, R., 1928. The life history of *Thysanoessa raschii*. J. Mar. Biol. Ass., U.K., 15: 57.

MacGinitie, G. E., 1955. Distribution and ecology of the marine invertebrates of Point Barrow, Alaska. Smithsonian Miscel. Coll., 128 (9): 201 pp.

MacIntyre, R. J., 1959. Gammarus: Some aspects of the genus with particular reference to *Gammarus oceanicus* from eastern Canada. McGill Univ. thesis: 112 pp. (MS).

Maclellan, Delphine C., 1967. The annual cycle of certain Calanoid species in West Greenland. Can. J. Zool., 45 (1): 101–115.

Margalef, R., 1963. On certain unifying principles in ecology. Amer. Nat., 97: 357–374.

Marshall, N. B., 1953. Egg size in Arctic, Antarctic and deep-sea fishes. Evolution, 7 (4): 328–341.

Marshall, S. M. and A. P. Orr, 1955. The Biology of a Marine Copepod. Edinburgh: Oliver & Boyd; 188 pp.

Matthew, W. D., 1915. Climate and evolution. Ann. N.Y. Acad. Sci., XXIV: 171–318.

Mayow, J., 1674. Tractatus Quinque Medico-Physici. Oxonii: e theatro Shildoniano.

Mayr, E., 1956. Geographical character gradients and climatic adaptation. Evolution, 10 (1): 105–108.

McLaren, I. A., 1960. On the origin of the Caspian and Baikal seals and the paleoclimatological implication. Amer. J. Sci., 258: 47–65.

McLaren, I. A., 1963. Effects of temperature on growth of zooplankton, and the adaptive value of vertical migration. J. Fish. Res. Bd. Canada, 20 (3): 685–727.

McLaren, I. A., 1964. Marine life in Arctic waters. In: Smith, I. N. (Ed.); The Unbelievable Land: 93–97. Ottawa: Queen's Printer.

McLaren, I. A., 1966. Adaptive significance of large body size and slow growth of the chaetognath *Sagitta elegans* in the Arctic. Ecology, 47: 852–855.

McWhinnie, M. A., 1964. Temperature responses and tissue respiration in Antarctic Crustacea with particular reference to the Krill *Euphausia superba*. Antarctic Res. Ser., 1: 63–72. American Geophysical Union.

Meguro, H., 1962. Plankton ice in the Antarctic Ocean. Antarctic Record, Tokyo, 14: 1192–1199.

Moore, H. B., 1934. The biology of *Balanus balanoides*. I. Growth rate and its relation to size, season and tidal level. J. Mar. Biol. Ass. U.K., 19: 851–868.

Moore, J. A., 1939. Temperature tolerance and rate of development in the eggs of Amphibia. Ecology, 20: 459–478.

Newell, N. D., 1962. Paleontological gaps and geochronology. J. Paleontol., 36: 592–610.

Newman, M. T., 1956. Adaptation of man to cold climates. Evolution, X (1): 101–105.

Nielsen, E. S., 1958. A survey of recent Danish measurements of the organic productivity in the sea. Conseil Permanent: Rapp. et Proc. Verb., 144: 92–95.

Northcote, T. G. and P. A. Larkin, 1956. Indices of productivity in British Columbia lakes. J. Fish. Res. Bd. Canada, 13: 515–540.

Odum, E. P., 1959. Fundamentals of Ecology. Philadelphia: W. B. Saunders, 2nd ed.; 546 pp.

Oliver, D. R., 1964. A limnological investigation of a large Arctic lake, Nettilling Lake, Baffin Island. Arctic, 17 (2): 69–83.

Olsen, S., 1955. A contribution to the systematics and biology of chaenichthyid fishes from South Georgia. Nytt Mag. f. Zool., 3: 79–93.

Orton, J. H., 1920. Sea-temperature, breeding and distribution in marine animals. J. Mar. Biol. Ass., U.K., 12: 339–366.

Orton, J. H., 1923. Some experiments on rate of growth in a polar region (Spitsbergen) and in England. Nature, 111: 146–148.

Peiss, C. N. and J. Field, 1950. The respiratory metabolism of excised tissue of warm- and cold-adapted fishes. Biol. Bull., 99: 213–224.

Pianka, E. R., 1966. Latitudinal gradients in diversity: A review of concepts. Amer. Nat., 100 (910): 33–46.

Provasoli, L. and I. J. Pintner, 1953. Ecological implications of in vitro nutritional requirements of algal flagellates. Ann. N.Y. Acad. Sci., 56 (5): 839–851.

Rasmussen, B., 1942. On dypvannsreken ved Spitsbergen. Rep. Norw. Fish. & Mar. Invest., 7 (4): 44 pp.

Rawson, D. S., 1958. Indices to lake productivity and their significance in predicting conditions in reservoirs and lakes with disturbed water levels. In: Larkin, P. A. (Ed.); H. R. Macmillan Lectures in Fisheries: 27–42. Univ. British Columbia.

Réaumur, R. A. F. de, 1735. Observations du thermomètre. Mém. Acad. Roy. Sci., Paris: 545–576.

Rensch, Bernhard, 1959. Evolution Above the Species Level. London: Methuen & Co.; 419 pp.

Rodbard, S., 1950. Weight and body temperature. Science, 111 (2887): 465–466.

Rodhe, W., 1955. Can plankton production proceed during winter darkness in subarctic lakes? Proc. Internat. Assoc. Theoret. and Applied Limnology, XII: 117–122.

Rosholt, J. N., C. Emiliani, J. Geiss, F. F. Koczy, and P. J. Wangersky, 1961. Absolute dating of deep-sea cores by the Pa^{231}/Th^{230} method. J. Geol., 69: 162–185.

Russell, F. S., 1932. On the biology of Sagitta. The breeding and growth of Sagitta elegans Verrill in the Plymouth area, 1930–31. J. Mar. Biol. Ass., U.K., 18 (1): 131–146.

Ruud, J. T., 1932. On the biology of southern Euphausiidae. Hvalrådets Skrifter, 2: 1–105.

Salomonsen, Finn, 1950. The Birds of Greenland. Copenhagen; Ejnar Munksgaard: 608 pp.

Salt, R. W., 1961. Resistance of poikilothermic animals to cold. Brit. Med. Bull., 17: 5–8.

Sars, G. O., 1895. An Account of the Crustacea of Norway, Vol. I, Amphipoda (plates). Christiania and Copenhagen: Alb. Cammermeyers Forlag.

Sars, G. O., 1903. An Account of the Crustacea of Norway, Vol. IV, Copepoda Calanoida. Bergen: Bergens Museum; 171 pp. plus plates.

Schneider, J. S., 1891. Fortplantningstiden og Livsvarigheden hos Amphipoderne. Tromsø Museums Aarshefter, 14: 59–74.

Scholander, P. F., 1955. Evolution of climatic adaptation in homeotherms. Evolution, 9 (1): 15–26.

Scholander, P. F., W. Flagg, V. Walters, and L. Irving, 1953. Climatic adaptation in Arctic and tropical poikilotherms. Physiol. Zool., XXVI (1): 67–92.

Scholander, P. F., R. Hock, V. Walters, and L. Irving, 1950. Adaptation to cold in Arctic and tropical mammals and birds in relation to body temperature, insulation and B.M.R. Biol. Bull., 99: 259.

Scholander, P. F., R. Hock, V. Walters, F. Johnson, and L. Irving, 1950. Heat regulation in some Arctic and tropical mammals and birds. Biol. Bull., 99: 237.

Scholander, P. F., L. van Dam, J. W. Kanwisher, H. T. Hammel, and M. S. Gordon, 1957. Supercooling and osmoregulation in Arctic fish. J. Cell. & Comp. Physiol., 49 (1): 5–24.

Scholander, P. F., V. Walters, R. Hock, and L. Irving, 1950. Body insulation of some Arctic and tropical mammals and birds. Biol. Bull., 99: 225.

Schroeder, E. H., 1963. North Atlantic temperatures at a depth of 200 meters. Serial Atlas Mar. Environment, Folio 2: 2 pp.; 9 charts.

Shen, Y-C., 1966. The distribution and morphological variation of certain euphausids and pelagic amphipods in tropical, northwest Atlantic and Canadian Arctic waters. McGill University thesis: 90 pp. (MS)

Sivertsen, E., 1935. Crustacea decapoda, euphausiacea and mysidacea of the Norwegian expeditions to east Greenland (1929, 1930, 1931, 1932). Skrifter om Svalbard og Ishavet, nr. 66: 41–54. Oslo.

Smith, E. H., F. M. Soule, and O. Mosby, 1937. The Marion and General Greene expeditions to Davis Strait and Labrador Sea, 1928–35. Scientific Results, part 2. Physical Oceanography. U.S. Treasury Dept., Coast Guard: Bull. No. 19; 259 pp.

Smith, R. E. and D. J. Hoijer, 1962. Metabolism and cellular function in cold acclimation. Physiol. Rev., 42 (1): 60–142.

Sörensen, T., 1953. A revision of the Greenland species of Puccinellia Parl. Medd. om Grönl., 136 (3): 1–179.

Spärck, R., 1936. On the relation between metabolism and temperature in some marine lamellibranchs and its ecological and zoogeographical importance. Kgl. Danske Vidensk. Selsk., Biol. Meddel, 13: 1–27.

Steele, D. H., 1961. Studies in the marine Amphipoda of eastern and northeastern Canada. McGill Univ. thesis: 350 pp. plus app. (MS).

Steele, V. J., 1964. Reproduction and metabolism in *Gammarus oceanicus* Segerstråle and *Gammarus setosus* Dementieva. McGill Univ. thesis: 165 pp. plus XV (MS).

Stephensen, K., 1923. Crustacea Malacostraca V. (Amphipoda I). Danish Ingolf Exped., III (8); 100 pp.

Stephensen, K., 1933a. Crustacea and Pycnogonidea. Medd. om Grönl., 104 (15): 1–12.

Stephensen, K., 1933b. Amphipoda. Medd. om Grönl., 79 (7): 1–88.

Stephensen, K., 1942. The Amphipoda of North Norway and Spitsbergen with adjacent waters. Tromsø Museums Skrifter, III (4): 363–526.

Stephensen, K., 1943. The zoology of East Greenland. Leptostraca, Mysidacea, Cumacea, Tanaidacea, Isopoda and Euphausiacea. Medd. om Grönl., 121 (10); 82 pp.

Stott, F. C., 1936. The marine food of birds in an inland fjord region in west Spitsbergen. J. Anim. Ecol., 5: 356–369.

Sverdrup, H. U., 1955. The place of physical oceanography in oceanographic research. J. Mar. Res., 14: 287–294.

Sverdrup, H. U., M. W. Johnson, and R. H. Fleming, 1946. The Oceans. Englewood Cliffs, N.J.: Prentice-Hall: 2nd ed.; 1087 pp.

Thompson, d'Arcy W., 1942. On Growth and Form. Cambridge Univ. Press; 1116 pp.

Thorson, G., 1936. The larval development, growth, and metabolism of Arctic marine bottom invertebrates compared with those of other seas. Medd. om Grönl., 100 (6), 155 pp.

Thorson, G., 1950. Reproductive and larval ecology of marine bottom invertebrates. Biol. Rev. 25: 1–45.

Thorson, G., 1952. Zur jetzigen Lage der marinen Bodentier-Ökologie. Verh. d. Deutschen Zool. Gesellsch. in Wilhelmshaven 1951 (34): 276–327.

Thorson, G., 1957. Bottom communities (sublittoral or shallow shelf). In: Treatise on marine ecology and paleoecology, Vol. 1, Geol. Soc. Amer. Mem., 67: 461–534.

Timofeev, V. T., 1960. Water Masses of the Arctic Basin. Hydrometeorological Publ., Leningrad (trans. by L. K. Coachman. Dept. of Oceanogr., Univ. of Washington, 1961); 190 pp.

Van't Hoff, T. H., 1884. Études de Dynamic Chimique. Amsterdam: Muller.

Wallace, A. R., 1878. Tropical Nature and Other Essays. London & New York: Macmillan; 356 pp.

Westlake, D. F., 1963. Comparisons of plant productivity. Biol. Rev., 38: 385–425.

Willett, H. C., 1953. Atmospheric and oceanic circulation as factors in glacial-interglacial changes of climate. In: Shapley, H. (Ed.); Climatic Change: 51–71, Cambridge, Mass.: Harvard Univ. Press.

Wilson, E. M. and P. Rickard, 1956. Frozen words. Polar Record, 8 (53): 95–108.

Wimpenny, R. W., 1941. Organic Polarity. Quart. Rev. Biol., 16: 389–425.

Wingfield, C. A., 1939. The activity and metabolism of poikilothermal animals in different latitudes–IV. Proc. Zool. Soc. Lond., Ser. A, 109 (1): 103–108.

Wiseman, J. D. H., 1954. The determination and significance of past temperature changes in the upper layer of the equatorial Atlantic Ocean. Proc. Roy. Soc. Lond., Ser. A, 222: 296–323.

Wohlschlag, D. E., 1960. Metabolism of an Antarctic fish and the phenomenon of cold adaptation. Ecology, 41 (2): 287–292.

Wohlschlag, D. E., 1963. An Antarctic fish with unusually low metabolism. Ecology, 44 (3), 557–564.

Wohlschlag, D. E., 1964. Respiratory metabolism and ecological characteristics of some fishes in McMurdo Sound, Antarctica. Antarctic Res. Ser. 1: 33–62. Amer. Geophys. Union.

Wynne-Edwards, V. C., 1952. Zoology of the Baird Expedition (1950). I. The birds observed in central and southeast Baffin Island. Auk: 69: 353–391.

Yaschnov, V. A., 1955. Morphology, distribution and systematics of Calanus finmarchicus s.l. Zool. Zhurnal, 34 (6): 1201–1223.

Yaschnov, V. A., 1961. Water masses and plankton. 1. Species of Calanus finmarchicus s.l. as indicators of definite water masses. Zool. Zhurnal, 40 (9): 1314–1334.

Zelikman, E. A., 1958. Distribution and breeding of Euphausids in the coastal zone of Murmansk. Akad. Nauk. SSSR., Proc. Murmansk. Biol. Sta. IV: 74–117.

Zenkevitch, L. A., 1949. Sur l'ancienneté de l'origine de la faune marine d'eau froide. XIIIe Congrès Int. Zool., 550.

Zenkevitch, L. A., 1961. Certain quantitative characteristics of the pelagic and bottom life of the ocean. In: Mary Sears (Ed.); Oceanography: 323–335. Washington; A.A.A.S.

AUTHOR INDEX

Allee, W. C., 9, 23, 24, 101
Allen, J. A., 25, 101
Amontons, 7
Antiphanes, 6
Apollonio, S., 49, 76, 101
Arrhenius, G., 33, 101
Arrhenius, S., 8, 101

Baker, J. R., 2, 101
Banner, A. H., 88, 101
Barghoorn, E. S., 35, 101
Barnard, J. L., 71, 97, 101
Barnard, K. H., 85, 89, 90, 101
Bary, B. M., 87, 101
Bateson, W., 86, 102
Bělehrádek, J., 9, 102
Berg, K., 13, 102
Bergmann, C., 24, 102
Bertram, G. C. L., 52, 102
Berzelius, 7
Bigelow, H. B., 90, 102
Black, R., 7
Bliss, L. C., 52, 53, 54, 102
Bogorov, B. G., 21, 102
Boyle, R., 7
Bramlette, M. N., 99, 102
Bray, J. R., 84, 102
Brodskii, K. A., 76, 102
Bruun, A. F., 56, 102
Bullock, T. H., 4, 10, 102
Bunt, J. S., 49, 76, 97, 102, 103
Bursa, A. S., 44, 46, 103
Burton, A. C., 4, 27, 103

Cairns, A. A., 21, 69, 103
Celsius, 7
Clausius, 72
Clément, 7
Cody, M. L., 93, 94, 103
Connell, J. H., 58ff, 62, 66, 93, 103
Conover, R. J., 14, 103
Coriolis, 41, 49
Cuvier, G., 72

Damon, P. E., 30, 103
Dampier, W. C., 7, 103
Dansereau, P., 51, 103
Darwin, C., 100
Dehnel, P. A., 19, 20
Demeusy, N., 13, 103
Désormes, 7
Digby, P. S. B., 21, 70, 103
Donn, W. L., 40ff, 96, 103, 105
Dorf, E., 33, 103

Downes, J. A., 51, 52, 53, 71, 95, 103
Drobysheva, S. S., 82, 89, 103, 104
Dunbar, M. J., 10, 18, 21, 30, 41, 43, 45, 58, 60, 66, 72, 74, 76, 82, 84, 88, 90, 104, 106

Edholm, O. G., 4, 27, 103
Einarsson, H., 21, 84, 85, 89, 104
Eiseley, L., 28, 104
Ekman, S., 71, 82, 104
El-Sayed, S. Z., 41, 105
Elton, C., 57, 58, 105
Emerson, A. E., 101
Emiliani, C., 31, 33, 105
Empedocles, 6
English, T. S., 54, 97, 105
Ericson, D. B., 30ff, 105
Ewing, M., 30ff, 96, 105

Fahrenheit, 7
Fairbridge, R. W., 33, 105
Ferguson-Wood, E. J., 37, 105
Field, J., 14, 110
Fischer, A. G., 58, 60, 72, 105
Flagg, W., 13, 111
Fleming, R. H., 42, 43, 112
Fontaine, M., 21, 45, 69, 105
Ford, E. B., 86, 105
Fox, H. M., 12ff, 19, 106
Fry, F. E. J., 4, 10, 14, 106

Galileo, 7
Good, D., 44, 51, 107
Gordon, M. S., 111
Grainger, E. H., 22, 47, 48, 88, 106
Gurjanova, E., 71, 106

Hammel, H. T., 111
Hammen, Th. van der, 33, 106
Hansen, H. J., 85, 88, 89, 106
Hartley, C. H., 41, 106
Harvey, H. W., 77, 78, 106
Haviland, M. D., 51, 54, 106
Hesse, R., 24, 106
Hildebrand, H. H., 20, 45, 106, 107
Hippocrates, 74
Hjort, J., 21, 107
Hock, R., 27, 111
Hoijer, D. J., 8, 111
Hutchinson, G. E., 58, 61, 66, 73, 82, 107
Huxley, J. S., 86, 107

ICNAF, 30, 107
Irving, L., 13, 27, 111

Jensen, A. S., 30, 107
Johnson, F., 27, 111
Johnson, M. W., 42, 43, 112

Kanwisher, J. W., 111
Kimble, G. H. T., 44, 51, 107
King, C. E., 58, 107
Klopfer, P. H., 58, 60, 107
Koczy, F. F., 31, 110
Krehl, L., 10, 107
Krogh, A., 10, 18, 107
Kusunoki, K., 41, 44, 45, 107

Lack, D., 94, 107
Larkin, P. A., 55, 109
Leicester, H. M., 7, 108
Leigh, E. G., 98, 108
Lindroth, C. H., 32, 108
Linnaeus, C., 18
Loeb, J., 18, 108
Löve, A., 32, 108
Löve, D., 32, 108

MacArthur, R. H., 58, 60, 61, 66, 73, 107, 108
Macdonald, R., 21, 108
MacGinitie, G. E., 76, 108
MacIntyre, R. J., 76, 108
Maclellan, D. C., 69, 88, 108
Mandelli, E., 41, 105
Margalef, R., 58, 72, 108
Marshall, N. B., 95, 108
Marshall, S. M., 21, 108
Matthew, W. D., 60, 108
Mayow, J., 9, 108
Mayr, E., 25, 109
McLaren, I. A., 8, 34, 68, 69, 109
McWhinnie, M. A., 14, 109
Meguro, H., 49, 109
Mendel, 100
Moore, H. B., 22, 109
Moore, J. A., 20, 109
Mosby, O., 42, 111

Newell, N. D., 60, 109
Newman, M. T., 25, 109
Newton, I., 7
Nielsen, E. S., 44, 47, 109
Nikitin, M. N., 76,102
Northcote, T. G., 55, 109

Odum, E. P., 61,109
Oliver, D. R., 55, 109
Olsen, S., 20, 109
Orias, E., 58ff, 62, 66, 93, 103
Orr, A. P., 21, 108
Orton, J. H., 18, 109, 110
Ostwald, 8

Peiss, C. N., 14, 110
Pianka, E. R., 58, 110
Pintner, I. J., 75, 110
Plato, 6
Poincaré, H., 100

Power, G., 14
Provasoli, L., 75, 110

Rasmussen, B., 21, 110
Rawson, D. S., 55, 110
Réaumur, R. A. F. de, 7, 9, 110
Rensch, B., 25, 110
Rickard, P., 6, 113
Rodbard, S., 26, 27, 110
Rodhe, W., 75, 77, 110
Rosholt, J. N., 31, 110
Russell, F. S., 21, 110
Ruud, J. T., 18, 21, 110

Salomonsen, F., 25, 110
Salt, R. W., 52, 110
Sanders, H. L., 63
Sars, G. O., 71, 86, 87, 110, 111
Schmidt, K. P., 24, 106
Schneider, J. S., 20, 111
Scholander, P. F., 13, 14, 23, 25, 27, 111
Schroeder, E. H., 43, 111
Shen, Y. C., 83, 111
Sivertsen, E., 82, 111
Smith, E. H., 42, 111
Smith, R. E., 8, 111
Soetbeer, F., 10, 107
Sörensen, T., 32, 111
Soule, F. M., 42, 111
Spärck, R., 12, 111
Steele, D. H., 78, 112
Steele, V. J., 82, 112
Stephensen, K., 82, 85, 90, 112
Stott, F. C., 41, 112
Sugimura, Y., 41, 105
Sverdrup, H. U., 32, 39, 40, 42, 43, 49, 112

Thompson, d'A. W., 72, 73, 112
Thorson, G., 12, 13, 18, 19, 59, 63, 68, 77, 95, 112
Timofeev, V. T., 41, 112

Van Dam, J. W., 111
Van't Hoff, T. H., 8, 47, 112

Wallace, A. R., 60, 72, 80, 113
Walters, V., 13, 27, 111
Wangersky, P. J., 31, 110
Westlake, D. F., 98, 113
Willett, H. C., 28, 113
Willis, 8
Wilson, E. M., 6, 113
Wimpenny, R. W., 19, 60, 113
Wingfield, C. A., 12ff, 113
Wiseman, J. D. H., 28, 29, 113
Wohlschlag, D. E., 15, 16, 17, 20, 54, 113
Wolff, T., 56, 102
Wollin, G., 30, 105
Wynne-Edwards, V. C., 59, 113

Yaschnov, V. A., 84, 88, 113

Zelikman, E. A., 89, 113
Zenkevitch, L. A., 34, 56, 113

SUBJECT INDEX

Acclimation, 4, 11, 14, 24
Acclimatization, 4, 11, 16, 24
Activity, 9ff, 16, 17, 20, 24, 94
Adaptation, 4, 11, 16, 18, 22, 23, 24, 34, 57, 74, 93
Algae, 49, 75
Allen's rule, 25
Amoeba, 9
Amphibia, 20, 71, 100
Amphipods, 18, 20, 45, 71, 76, 78, 82, 83, 84, 85
Annelida, 83
Antarctic, 4, 14, 16, 18, 24, 28, 38, 41, 42, 49, 73, 76, 92, 97
Antarctic convergence, 42, 43
Arctia caja, 20
Arctic char, 22
  convergence, 42
  definition, 23, 43
  ocean, 31ff, 38ff, 65, 92, 96
  water, 3, 17
  zone, 38ff, 44, 52, 87

Balanus balanoides, 22
Benthos, 13, 18, 19, 22, 50, 56, 77, 83, 95
Bergmann's rule, 24ff, 70
Bering Strait, 32
Biogeography, 56, 80ff
Biomass, 77, 93, 98
Birds, 2, 23, 24, 26, 58, 59, 71, 93ff, 100
Body size, 20, 24ff, 67, 68ff, 75, 77ff
Boreo-Arctic, 83
Boreogadus saida, 14
Breeding cycles, 18, 20, 21, 68ff, 76, 79, 99

Cabbeling, 42
Calanus, 69, 87, 89, 90
Calanus finmarchicus, 21, 84, 88
  glacialis, 88
  helgolandicus, 88
  hyperboreus, 88
Caribou, 24
Catalysis, 7
Cenozoic, 100
Chaetognaths, 18, 21, 69
Climate, as ecological factor, 93ff
Climatic change, 2, 29, 34, 37, 47, 60, 72, 80, 92, 95, 99
Climatic maximum, 28, 29, 96
Clutch size, 93ff
Cod, 22, 23
Cod, polar, 14
Coelenterates, 72
Cold hardiness, 22, 23

Collembola, 71
Competition, 3, 93, 98
Copepods, 9, 14, 21, 45, 69, 70, 71, 76, 84, 87
Coral reefs, 98
Coregonus sardinella, 15, 20
Coriolis, 41, 49
Cretaceous, 58
Crustacea, 71
Cryptomorphs, 87
Cyprina islandica, 30

Daphnia, 9
Detritus, 65, 75
Devonian, 100
Discoasters, 30
Dissolved organic substances, 37, 75
Distribution, 2, 3, 5, 80ff

Earthworm, 72
Ecosystem, 57, 59, 73, 77, 80ff, 88ff, 100
Ecosystem, age of, 3, 49, 50
  complexity of, 3, 36, 45, 61ff, 74, 81, 87, 90, 95, 99
  maturity of, 1, 4, 49, 59, 71, 72ff
  stability of, 61, 66, 72ff, 90, 93ff
Egg size, 18, 68, 73, 74, 78
  number, 18, 68ff, 74, 93ff
Energy, 7, 10, 15, 16, 20, 22, 36, 37, 64ff, 73, 98
  sharing of, 11, 16, 17, 93ff
Entropy, 73
Enzymes, 7, 16
Eukrohnia hamata, 21
Euphausia superba, 14
Euphausids, 21, 69, 82, 85
Evolution, 4, 57, 58, 68, 72, 73, 77, 99, 100
Extinction, 60, 72, 73, 74, 99

Fats, 24, 27
Fecundity, 3, 18, 69, 70, 73, 74
Feldmark, 54
Fishery, 45
Fishes, 15ff, 20, 22, 23, 45, 71, 72, 95
Food supply, 11, 17, 19, 24, 65, 68, 75, 76, 77, 94, 95, 99
Foraminifera, 28ff, 100
Frozen words, 6

Gadus morhua, 22
Gadus ogac, 23
Gammaridae, 84
Gammarus, 84

117

Gammarus oceanicus, 76, 82
  setosus, 76
  wilkitzki, 76
Glacial climate, 2, 3, 4
Glaciation, 3, 28ff, 50, 96, 97
Greeks, 6
Grouse, 24
Growth rate, 9, 18ff, 38, 39, 52, 65, 68, 70, 77
Gulf Stream, 49

Habitat, 34, 57, 75, 83, 90, 93, 96ff
Heat, 7, 9, 23, 49
Heat, caloric theory of, 7
  conservation of, 24
  exchangers, 24, 27
  kinetic theory of, 7
  solar, 36
Hibernation, 22, 23, 24, 27
Homotherms, 8, 23ff, 57
Hyperia galba, 85, 90
  spinigera, 85, 90

Ice, 2, 5, 23, 31, 45, 49, 97
Ice age, 28ff, 56, 60, 96
Icebergs, 32
Ice flora, 49, 76, 97
Idus melanotus, 14
Insects, 20, 22, 51, 94, 95, 96
Insulation, 23, 27
Islands, 62
Isopoda, 84

Jurassic, 100

Krogh line, 14

Lakes, 54, 55, 96
Larval stages, 19, 22, 77
Lepidoptera, 20
Life cycles, 20ff, 68ff
Light, 2, 36ff, 49, 75, 76, 92
Locomotion, 9, 68
Lysianassidae, 84

Mammals, 23, 24, 26, 27, 71
Mediterranean, 34, 82
Meganyctiphanes norvegica, 82, 89
Mesidothea sabini, 84
Mesozoic, 23, 57, 100
Metabolism, 9, 10, 11ff, 18, 19, 38, 68, 70, 77, 94
Migration, 24, 51, 92, 94
Miocene, 34
Mollusca, 83
Morphs, 79, 81ff, 86
Myoxocephalus scorpius, 23

Nekton, 16
Nerves, conductivity of, 24, 27
Niche, 57, 58, 59, 60, 75, 80, 83, 90, 93
Nutrients, 37ff, 53, 65, 92

Oedicerotidae, 84
Oligocene, 33
Orfe, 14
Oscillation, adaptation to, 66, 68ff, 74
  environmental, 1, 3, 36, 38, 47, 50, 51, 56, 66ff, 77, 78, 92ff, 99
  population, 61, 66, 74
Otter, 24

Pandalus borealis, 21
Parathemisto gaudichaudi, 82, 85, 89, 90
  libellula, 76
Pectinaria auricoma, 13
  granulata, 13
  koveni, 13
Penguins, 24
Permafrost, 52
Permian, 57, 100
Phocinae, 34
Phytoplankton, 10, 19, 39, 50, 76
Plankton, 14, 16, 47, 64, 83, 95
Plants, temperature compensation in, 10
Pleistocene, 2, 3, 5, 6, 23, 28ff, 50, 56, 58, 60, 73, 92, 96, 99, 100
Pleustidae, 84
Pliocene, 23, 31ff, 57, 58, 92, 99, 100
Plover, 25
Poikilotherms, 6ff, 11ff, 16, 18, 20, 23
Polar Bear, 26
Poles, migration of, 31, 56, 92
Predation, 93, 94, 95, 98
Production, 37ff, 45, 49, 51, 53, 55, 65ff, 92, 93, 98
Production, factors determining, 2, 37ff, 49, 65ff
Productivity, 1, 3, 37ff, 61, 93, 98
Proximate level, 1, 2ff, 20, 66, 68, 80, 92
Pseudocalanus, 69, 84
Pseudocalanus minutus, 21

Q-10 law, 8, 10, 14
Quaternary, 28, 33

Racoon, 24
Rain forest, 59, 63, 64, 96, 98
Rana catesbiana, 20
  sylvatica, 20
Recent, 28, 96
Reptiles, 71, 100
Respiration, 9
Rigophila dearborni, 15

Sagitta, 70
Sagitta elegans, 21, 69
Salvelinus alpinus, 22
Salvelinus fontinalis, 14
Scotland, 31, 32
Sculpin, 23
Selection, 2, 66ff, 74, 77, 100
Soil, 53, 96
Speciation, 57, 58, 79, 90, 93, 99
Species, 18, 86

Species diversity, 36, 57, 58, 61, 66, 71ff, 77ff, 93, 98
Speckled trout, 10, 14
Stability, of ecosystem, 61, 66, 67, 72ff, 93ff
  environmental, 61, 93
  hydrographic (vertical), 2, 19, 39ff, 45, 49, 65, 66, 92
Standing crop, 38, 47, 61, 65
Stenothermy, 15
Stenothoidae, 84
Step-clines, 99
Subantarctic, 43, 85
Subarctic, 17, 18, 19, 43ff, 65, 73, 84, 85, 98
Systematics, 18, 80ff

Temperature, absolute scale, 1
  adaptation to low, 1ff, 6ff, 57, 91
  compensation for, 10
  as controlling factor, 1ff, 6ff, 21, 22, 26, 27, 34, 38ff
Tertiary, 32ff, 58
Thermogenesis, 8
Thysanoessa inermis, 21, 82, 85, 88, 89, 90
  longicaudata, 21, 82, 85, 88, 89

neglecta, 85, 89, 90
raschii, 21, 82, 85, 89, 90
Tiger moth, 20
Time, as ecological factor, 3, 49, 59ff, 93, 99
Tree limit, 51, 71, 97
Trematomus bernacchii, 15
Tropical fauna, 10, 83
Tundra, 53, 59

Uca pugilator, 13
Ultimate level, 2ff, 11, 19ff, 68, 70
Upwelling, 41, 65

Variation, intraspecific, 83, 84ff, 93, 99

Westwoodilla, 84
Whitefish, 15, 22
Winter growth, 75
Winter spawning, 76, 99
Wyville-Thompson Ridge, 31ff, 43

Zooplankton, 45, 75